MASTERING MASONRY

MASTERING MASONRY

How to Work
with Bricks
Blocks, Concrete
and Stone

KENNETH J. NOLAN

jD JONATHAN DAVID PUBLISHERS, INC
MIDDLE VILLAGE, NY 11379

MASTERING MASONRY

by
Kenneth J. Nolan

Copyright © 1980
by
Jonathan David Publishers, Inc.

Address all inquiries to:

Jonathan David Publishers, Inc.
68-22 Eliot Avenue
Middle Village, New York 11379

Library of Congress Cataloging in Publication Data

Nolan, Kenneth J. 1943–
    Mastering masonry.

    1. Masonry--Amateurs' manuals. I. Title.
TH5313.N64   693'.1   80-22194
ISBN 0-8246-0261-7

Printed in the United States of America

To my father, who taught me
never to give up,
And my kids, who never let me.

CONTENTS

Preface

Masonry is an art. Over the years American masons have proven this by building beautiful, durable structures of all kinds.

Of course, to become a skilled mason requires years of training and experience (most masons undergo a three-year apprenticeship program). Nevertheless, once the amateur understands the fundamentals of masonry, he can undertake and successfully complete many projects.

Mastering Masonry is designed to acquaint the reader with the materials and techniques used by the mason. If you decide to undertake projects of your own, you will find the step-by-step instructions, the photographs, the charts and diagrams, and the time and energy-saving hints very helpful. Should you decide to hire a contractor for a complicated project at any time in the future, an understanding of the material covered in this book will equip you to make the best choice of contractor and to oversee the job with confidence.

If you are among the millions of people trying to save money on home improvements, this book is for you. Once you have begun to undertake projects of your own, you will find that the money spent by you each year for home improvements and repairs will decrease considerably.

I suggest that you read *Mastering Masonry* from beginning to end, then refer to specific chapters as the need arises. Remember that the real secret to good masonry is planning ahead carefully. Remember, too, that no man is born with a trowel in his hand: he has to be taught by someone.

Good luck!

Kenneth J. Nolan

Acknowledgments

Many thanks to the following for the information, photographs, and diagrams they so graciously supplied:

Binghamton Brick Company, Inc.
Bowen Building Block and Supply Company
Brick Institute of America
Department of the Army
Diamond Expansion Bolt Company
Don Burkhart, Stamm Supply Company
Goldblatt Tool Company
Franklin Glue Company
Heatilator, Inc.
L.P. Butts
Pittsburg Corning Corporation
Protective Coating Company
Sakrete, Inc.
Seward Sand and Gravel, Inc.
Vega Industries, Inc.
W.R. Grace and Company

MASTERING
MASONRY

1

LAYING OUT AND EXCAVATING

Before you decide to call an excavating contractor, try to figure out some of the problems that will occur during the actual work. Do you have very sandy soil? Are there lot of large rocks or trees for removal? Will you need fill brought in or fill removed? Is there a problem with drainage? An excavating contractor will ask you these questions and you should be prepared to answer them.

Contact more than one excavator. This way you will have more than one opinion on how your job ought to be done, and more than one price. Check the reputation of the contractor if you can, and always get a written contract. This will prevent misunderstanding.

What Will It Cost?

Excavating contractors usually quote on a complete job. The quote will be for digging and backfilling the job. Moving large piles of dirt or hauling it long distances to or from your job, might be an extra. This is where a contract would be advisable.

After discussing your particular situation with the contractor, you might reach a per day price, or a per hour price. The price he charges will vary with the locality, but it might be in the range of $18.00 to $25.00 per hour. Prices also vary with the type of equipment required to do the job. Most excavators charge by the hour. This might sound like a high price per hour but if you think how long it would take to dig by hand it doesn't sound so bad. Remember also that these big machines cost tens of thousands of dollars to purchase and large amounts to keep in tip top shape.

Save That Top Soil

In a large excavation the top soil becomes a valuable item. Have the contractor scrape the top soil off the excavation area, and push or haul it away to a pile for later use. It can be spread around the project after the job has been backfilled. A 50″ X 50″ excavation contains about 60 cubic yards of topsoil. If you had to buy this amount of top soil you would have to spend hundreds of dollars for it.

Laying Out the Area With Instruments

You can rent the professional leveling instruments needed, but if you hire a contractor to excavate, he should have his own. No one can accurately "eyeball" the correct depth. If the contractor tells you that he can, just say you want to get a second opinion.

A level and transit are both used to survey and lay out buildings. The transit is like a telescope with lines or

Light construction level transit. Used for elevations, landscape, plumb walls, and uprights.

Builder's level. Levels quickly and accurately.

cross hairs in the scopes and adjusting screws that are used to line up exact angles. Once it has been set up on its stand (tripod) and adjusted to be level at the base, the transit or level can be turned around to lay out angles or elevations. The leveling scope can be released to pivot vertically in a transit, while it remains stationary in a builder's or "dumpy" level.

Whether you use a level or a level-transit, the first step is to locate a flat spot upon which to set the instrument. The spot should be away from where you plan to excavate. That way it can be set in the same place time and time again if it had to be used again. First, set up the tripod base for the instrument and then set the level carefully on the base. Level the transit or level on the base using the bubble in the level. This isn't very hard if you have set up the tripod on a fairly flat surface. Hold the level with both hands on the adjusting screws and turn the opposite sides at the same time to make adjusting easier. Once the leveling screws are snug against the base, swing the scope around to make sure it reads level in any position. Make the necessary adjustments until it reads, level all around the 360° base. If you didn't have the level exactly level on its base you will get readings that would become more inaccurate as the distance increases.

Leveling rods and targets are made from solid maple and have deeply registered black graduations and numbers on a weatherproof background. Foot numerals are in red and inches down to ⅛ inches. The target reads down to 1/64 of an inch. Rods are two sections with an open height of 10 feet.

It is possible to make a rod yourself out of a three or four inch wide board, eight feet long. Use a long ruler taped to the board or measurements marked on the board and you have created yourself a rod. The object of the rod and target is to help in establishing elevations away from the level or transit-level. What you are actually doing is sighting a level line through the scope to the rod, showing whether the ground is higher or lower at that point.

If the project you are working on is a small one and you don't want to involve yourself with renting or borrowing a transit or level, you can use a line level and a hand level.

A line level is attached to the line by hooks and can be slid along the line. After you attach the line to one stake, you can stretch it tight and attach the line level. It will show you if you have to raise or lower the line before you attach it at the next stake. If you repeat this around the perimeter of your project you can see if the surface is out of level at the stakes. The tight line will be level and you can measure down to the ground at any point along the line to see the difference in elevations.

Before you proceed any further, check to see if there are any large stones or other obstacles in the inside of your project. It will be much easier to remove them now then to have a backhoe dig a trench for a wall and then try to remove them.

To get ready for the actual laying out of the building you should get some 2″ × 4″ boards and make stakes 24″ long. If your project is a square or a rectangular shape you will need 16 stakes. At each corner you will have one stake showing the corner and three stakes to hold up the batter board. The batter board is made to hold up the lines, when you have established a corner. You can use furring strips for the batter boards, which are set up about three feet outside the actual excavation so they won't be in the way of digging and can be used later if needed.

Assuming your building is square or rectangular in shape, start by laying out the stakes from a boundary line or existing building. First, measure from this line or building to a point where one of the finished corners is to be. Drive in a sharpened stake here. After driving in the stake, hammer a nail into the top. This will allow you to tie off a line from corner to corner. Erect a batter board about 36" behind the stake at about the same right angle as the corner of the building.

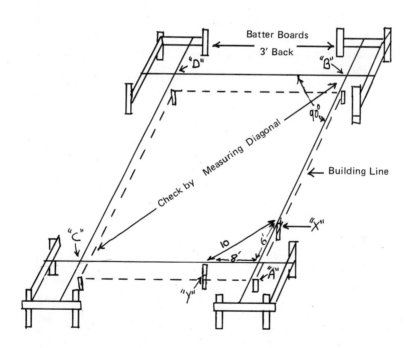

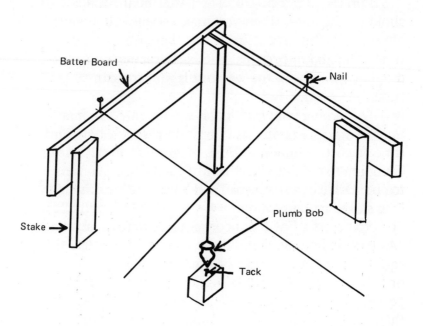

Measure the distance from the first stake to the finished wall. Drive in a sharpened stake. Always check your measurements twice to eliminate any errors. Erect a batter board three feet behind the stake, again at right angles to the wall line.

Next, measure the width of the building, and drive in a second set of stakes. To find if you have your stakes square with each other, measure the diagonals. The diagonals should be the same.

Next, erect a set of batter boards behind the other stakes, the same way as before. Look over the situation to be sure the batter boards all face correctly and are all about the same height. Now, stretch a mason's line (it will stretch without breaking) from corner to corner over the stakes and tie it to the batter boards. Don't tie the line off tight yet as you might have to make some adjustments.

Measure off a distance of 8 feet from corner "A" along wall line "A-B" and drive in a small stake here, point "X". Now measure along the wall line "A-C" from the stake in corner "A" 6 feet to a point "Y" and drive in a stake. Move the lines that are stretched between "A" and "B" or "C" until the distance from "X-Y" is 10 feet. This will prove the corner 90°. You may have to move the stake at point "A" to the exact point where the two lines meet. This can be done with a plumb bob. Tie the lines off tight on the batter boards. Next, move to the next corner, point "C". You have already made line "A-B" square with line "A-C". Don't move the line now. Line "C-D" can be squared off the same as lines "A-B" and "A-C" were. Once you have line "C-D" squared with "A-C", tie it off tightly at the batter board on corner "D". When you think you have the corners perfectly square, check the diagonals again. If the lines that are drawn from batter board to batter board are correct, put small nails in close to the lines on the batter boards so that if you want to take the lines down and replace them at any time you will be able to.

Some points to think about: Batter boards can be made out of scrap lumber but they should be level at the top and driven into the ground far enough so the vibration of a machine working near won't loosen them. Also, if it is possible to keep the batter boards at the same height, it will be a lot easier to stretch your lines.

The transit level or builders level are handy in setting the batter boards at the same height. A water level is excellent for this purpose and is also excellent to use for setting forms. Water levels are extremely accurate and very inexpensive compared to transit or builder's levels.

By setting back the batter boards behind the building lines you won't have to remove them when digging begins and you can dig the hole wide enough so that

8

you can get beside the finished wall, to work on it. The depth you dig your hole will govern the height of your foundation wall. Take all your measurements for the elevations from the highest point on your sight. This will save excavation costs. Have your wall height figured so that your wall will extend out of the ground enough to keep the wood sill or siding from touching the ground. This will help prevent rot and termites. Before excavating, pour hydrated lime from a can around the building line you establish, to help the excavator.

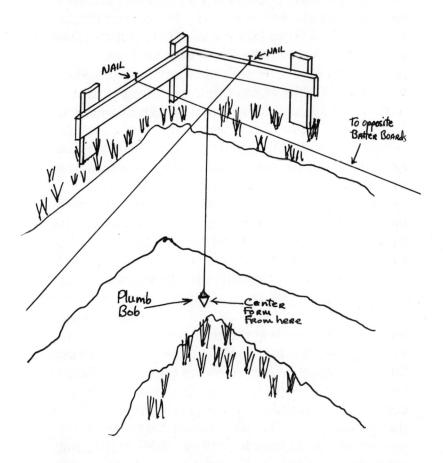

At this point, you can take down the lines and begin excavating. After excavating put lines back on the batter boards where you marked them with a nail. Stretch the lines tight. At the points where they intersect in the corners you can use a plumb bob to re-establish the corners of the building. Drive a stake in under the plumb bob.

If the excavation is relatively level, you can start at any corner and build forms. The forms are usually made out of 2″ × 8″ boards with stakes made out of 2″ × 4″ boards driven into the ground on the outside of the forms. The stakes should be no more than 4″ apart. If possible, put them closer. They hold the forms from lifting and sliding sideways. Use furring strips or scrap lumber to hold the forms across the top. Since you will have to remove the forms after the concrete hardens, it is wise to use duplex headed nails--which are made for form work.

The easiest way to set up forms is to build them around the outside first, using a 48″ level to get the top of the board level. Then working with the level, set the inside boards. If you cut all the furring strips or other boards used to hold the top of the forms apart, the same length it will make the work easier. The same holds true for the side boards used in the form work. All wood used in form work can be cleaned off and used later.

The forms should be built so the footing will be at least 12″ wider than the finished wall. Since it distributes the load of the building on the ground, the footing should be at least 8″ thick and below the frost line. Check with the local building codes for the depth you should make your footing in the ground, as the depth frost penetrates in the ground is different all over the country.

Protect your footing and foundation from water, the biggest problem you might encounter. Place drain tile around the perimeter even with the top of the footing with a slope to drain the water away.

Here is a chart to help in estimating the amount of concrete needed in footings for block foundations in cubic yards.

Width of Wall	Width and Thickness of Footing	Length of Footing Around Perimeter 20'	30'	40'	50'	100'
6" block	12" wide 8" thick	½	¾	1	1½	2½
8" block	16" wide 8" thick	¾	1	1¼	1¾	3¼
10" block	20" wide 10" thick	1	1½	2	2½	5¼
12" block	24" wide 12" thick	1½	2¼	3	3¾	7½

A builder's dumpy level. Used to level forms, to square corners, and to check elevations. Tripod has adjustable legs.

Line level. Can be attached to a line that is pulled tight in order to check levels. Although not as accurate as a builder's level, it is useful in setting up forms.

A man holding a grading rod, which is very useful for setting concrete forms. The rod is used with a level or transit.

This is one way to make a batter board. It is set up before the excavation is done. It is later used to establish building lines.

2

CONCRETE

What Is Concrete?

Concrete is a mixture of cement, water, and aggregates. Sand makes up its "fine aggregates." Stone of various sizes makes up its "coarse aggregates."

Concrete is a strong and versatile building material which if care is taken to construct properly, should last indefinitely. It also requires a minimum amount of maintenance, is fire resistant, has high compressive strength, and is resistant to water to a degree.

Natural cement has been around for a few hundred years. Since it is made of a natural formation of clay and limestone, it varies in composition, and thus in strength. Portland cement isn't a brand name, it is a type of cement. The name "Portland" came from the place where it was discovered. Portland cement is available in different types. Type 1 is for normal service. It is available in grey and white and also air-entrained. Type 2 generates less heat during curing and is more resistant to sulfate attack. Type 3 is a high early strength cement and may be used when it desired to get maximum strength in just a few days.

Portland cement is made by crushing limestone, clay, and shale (or slag) to produce a proper combination of materials. The mixture is then fired in a large kiln at about 3,000 degrees to form clinkers, which are cooled and ground into powder. A small amount of gypsum is then added to regulate the setting time and the cement is ready for shipment either in bags or in bulk tanks.

A bag of Portland cement weighs 94 pounds and is one cubic foot in volume. When you mix Portland cement with water you get what is called cement paste. Cement should be 10% to 12% of a concrete mix; the rest should be aggregate.

Aggregates

Fine aggregates are sand and small pebbles or pieces of crushed stone that will pass through a ¼ inch mesh screen. The sand should be clean and well graded. "Well graded" aggregate ranges in size from fine to coarse. A well graded aggregate will need less cement and make stronger concrete.

Coarse aggregates are gravel or crushed stone. They should be clean, hard and free of impurities, such as dirt and clay. Coarse aggregates should range in size from ¼ inch up to 2 inches; the type of work determining the size of the coarse aggregates. A good rule to follow is to use coarse aggregate no larger than ¼ the thickness of the work.

If you are mixing the concrete yourself, you can go to a building supply yard and find that they have aggregates in different sizes in bulk quantities. They also sell bags of premixed concrete and of sand.

Characteristics of Aggregates

Characteristic	Significance or importance	Test or practice ASTM designation	Specification requirement
RESISTANCE TO ABRASION	Index of aggregate quality. Warehouse floors, loading platforms, pavements.	C131	Max. percent loss*
RESISTANCE TO FREEZING AND THAWING	Structures subjected to weathering.	C290.C291	Max. number of cycles
CHEMICAL STABILITY	Strength and durability of all types of structures	C227 (mortar bar) C289 (chemical) C586 (aggregate prism) C295 (petrographic)	Max. expansion of mortar bar* Aggregates must not be re-active with cement alkalies*
PARTICLE SHAPE AND SURFACE TEXTURE	Workability of fresh concrete		Max. percent flat and elongated pieces
GRADING	Workability of fresh concrete Economy	C136	Max. and min. percent passing standard sieves
BULK UNIT WEIGHT	Mix design calculations. Classification	C29	Max. or min. unit weight (special concrete)
SPECIFIC GRAVITY	Mix design calculations.	C127 (coarse aggregate) C128 (fine aggregate)	
Absorption and surface moisture	Control of concrete quality.	C70, C127, C128	

*Aggregates not conforming to specification requirements may be used if service records or performance tests indicate they produce concrete having the desired properties.

Sand Must Be Clean

To find out if the sand is dirty, you can conduct a test that is very simple. Use a one quart jar. Put about 2 inches of the sand in the jar and add water until the jar is ¾ full. Cover the jar and shake it vigorously for a minute, then let the jar stand overnight so the sand will settle completely. The layer of silt will settle at the top of the sand. If this layer is more than ⅛ inch thick, then the sand is not clean enough for concrete.

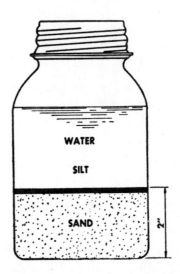

Quart-jar method of determining silt content of sand.

Some people have been told that "bank run" gravel is good for use in concrete. "Bank run" is gravel from a gravel bank or edge of an old stream bank. Most of these deposits will have an excessive amount of sand to gravel causing you to have to use more cement in mixing. There is also a chance of having a certain amount of impurities in the finer aggregates causing substandard concrete. Avoid using "bank run."

Clean Water Is a Must

The water used in mixing concrete should be free of any impurities such as oil, salt, and alkali. A good rule to remember is that if the water is fit to drink, it is fit for use in concrete.

Air-Entrained Concrete

Air-entrained concrete is easier to work with, mixes better and is more durable and weather resistant than non-air-entrained. It should be used where freezing and thawing affect the concrete (e.g. sidewalks, driveways, etc). Air-entrained concrete contains an agent which forms millions of tiny bubbles of air in the concrete. The air bubbles allow the concrete to expand when it freezes. Water trapped in the concrete expands and fills the void left by the air-entrained agent.

Lightweight Concrete

Concrete usually weighs about 150 pounds per cubic foot. It can be made lighter by the use of lightweight aggregates. Lightweight aggregates also increase the insulating qualities of concrete and the fire resistance.

Lightweight aggregates are usually made of cinders, clay shale, or slag. They make concrete that weigh between 100 and 130 pounds per cubic foot. It is possible to make concrete that weighs as little as 50 pounds per cubic foot by using lightweight materials such as pumice or mika as aggregates. Concrete made of lightweight materials is usually used for fire protection and in making such things as precast slabs, and built-up roofs; it should never be used where any load will be placed on it.

Additives for Concrete

Concrete additives are usually used to help improve workability, speed set up time and make the concrete harder. If care is taken and the user follows directions given with the additives, he will get very good results.

Sometimes, fine powdered lime or pumice is added to improve the workability of the mix. It should be remembered that they reduce the overall strength of the concrete. It is always safer to add more Portland cement to a mix to improve the workability or to pour the cement at a slower rate to keep ahead of the setting.

Calcium chloride may be added to a mix to help it set faster. About 1½ pounds of calcium chloride is added to a 94 pound bag of Portland. It is best to add the calcium chloride while mixing to spread it through the mix more completely.

Storing Cement

Portland cement can be stored for long periods of time if kept dry. If the bags get damp, the cement will begin to set in the bags. Some lumps may occur in the stored bags, but that can also be from being stacked too long. If you can squeeze the lumps in your hand and turn them into powder then the cement is OK to use. If it is too hard, throw away the whole bag.

Coloring Concrete

Colored concrete is made in many colors. The colors are durable because they are usually uniform through the slab or wall. The color fades, but only slightly. The use of coloring in concrete gives you many options in decorating.

The different ways to color concrete are: 1. Adding the coloring to the mix as it is being mixed. 2. Working the color into the surface of the concrete before it drys out. 3. Using colored stone and exposing the stone as a final finish (this is called "exposed aggregate finish"). Below is a table on materials which make particular colors. If you want to achieve better coloring, use white Portland cement and white sand. However, regular Portland and aggregates will still make the same colors. If you use about 9 pounds of coloring to a 94 pound bag of Portland, you will be close to the color you desire. You can change the ratio slightly to suit your desired color.

Color	Mix
White	White Portland and White Sand
Brown	Brown Oxide of Iron
Green	Chromium Oxide
Gray	Normal Coloring of Concrete
Rose Red	Red Oxide of Iron
Pink	Red Oxide of Iron (half as much as for Red Rose)
Cream	Yellow Oxide of Iron

It is very important to mix the same proportion of coloring with the same amount of concrete each time. Weigh or measure the amounts you use and keep a record of them.

Mixing Concrete

Concrete mixes are usually figured using three numbers. For example: a 1:2:3 mix would mean that you would use one part of Portland cement, two parts clean sand, and three parts stone or gravel. Different mixes are used for different degrees of strength required in concrete.

Example:

Type of work	Cement	Proportions Sand	Gravel	Gallons of Water Required Wet Sand	Moist Sand	Dry Sand
Thin — 2-4"	1 bag	2 cubic ft.	2 cubic ft.	3½ gal.	3¾ gal.	4½ gal.
Water-resistant Wear-resistant	1 bag	2 cubic ft.	3 cubic ft.	3¾ gal.	4½ gal.	5½ gal.
Normal Reinforced Work	1 bag	2½ cubic ft.	3½ cubic ft.	4½ gal.	5 gal.	6½ gal.
Large Areas (footings, foundations)	1 bag	3 cubic ft.	5 cubic ft.	5 gal.	6 gal.	7 gal.

The sand and gravel in the mix may be changed to make the mix more workable but *Never* change the ratio of the cement to water. The more water you add, the less wearability the concrete will have.

To find the moisture of sand, pick up a small handful and squeeze it in the palm of your hand. If the sand forms a ball that stays together and/or is firm, then it is considered wet. If the sand forms a ball and, as you open your hand, falls apart and crumbles, it is considered to be damp. If you can't form a ball with it and it just slides out of your hand, then it is dry. A sandpile may look drier than it really is and that is why it is important that you make this simple test. It is an important part of correct proportioning and can affect the overall quality of the concrete.

After you have mixed your first batch of concrete, either in a small mixer or in a wheelbarrow, you should check it for workability. Concrete should be smooth, plastic and thoroughly mixed. If it contains too much water, it will run and the large and small aggregates will separate causing a weak finish. If it is too dry, you will have trouble moving it in your forms and getting it to fill all the corners and holes. You will also have trouble leveling it and it could set up before you have a chance to properly finish it. If it is too wet, add a small amount of sand and aggregates to get the right mix. If it is stiff, add cement and water in as near a ratio to the original mix as possible. *Never* add water without adding cement as this will weaken the mix.

Hand Mixing

Hand mixing is easy if the project is small. You can use premeasured mixed concrete soil in bags or you can buy sand and gravel in bags alone with Portland cement and make your own concrete mix. A check with your local building supply dealer will save you some time and energy. Some of these dealers stock sand and gravel in bulk which they sell in any quantities needed to mix your own. Large amounts should be delivered as sand and stone are quite heavy. Most dealers will help you figure the amount of sand, stone and cement you need.

If you decide to mix your own, you will need some tools and a wheelbarrow. You can mix in the wheelbarrow or in a motor-driven mixer. A shovel, hoe, and 5 gallon pail are also needed. Using a motor-driven mixer will save you valuable time and energy when it comes to screening and finishing your work. A machine usually mixes the concrete more thoroughly. However, unless you are lucky enough to have a neighbor who is the owner of a mixer (and allows you to use it), you will have the expense of renting a mixer. You will have to go and get it, clean it out and bring it back when finished. All of this adds to the time a project will take.

You can rent concrete mixers, motor mixers, bull-floats, trowels, finishing machines, and vibrators from rental dealers, such as Taylor Rental, which has locations all over the country. A check in the phone book will help locate one.

Concrete mixer. This mixer is equipped with road wheels enabling it to be towed to the site. The drum of a concrete mixer has fixed paddles that revolve with the drum.

If you are mixing concrete yourself, start with a small amount of water either in the mixer or wheelbarrow. Add the aggregates and cement and remaining water as needed. Use a pail to add the water. Mark on the side of the pail the amount of water you need for the mix. This will allow you to have the same amount each time.

Sand is sold either by the ton or by the "cubic yard." You will have to check with your local dealer. The table below is figured in pounds.

Estimating Concrete Required (in yards)

Concrete Needed	Cement	Sand	Stone	Water (Maximum)
¼ cubic yard	2 bags	350 lbs.	500 lbs.	12 gals.
½ cubic yard	3 bags	700 lbs.	1,000 lbs.	18 gals.
1 cubic yard	6 bags	1,400 lbs.	2,000 lbs.	36 gals.

Mortar mixer. This mixer is designed for mixing mortar for brick, block, and stone work. Like the concrete mixer, it has road wheels. The drum is stationary and the paddles move around on a shaft, which mixes the mortar more thoroughly.

Estimating Desired Thickness of Concrete	Area in Square Feet (Width X Length)					
	50	100	150	200	250	300
2" thick	3/8 yd.	5/8 yd.	7/8 yd.	1-1/4	1-1/2	1-7/8
4" thick	5/8	1-1/4	1-7/8	2-1/2	3	3-3/4
6" thick	1	1-7/8	2-7/8	3-7/8	4-1/2	5-1/2
8" thick	1-1/4	2-1/2	3-7/8	5	6-1/4	7-1/2

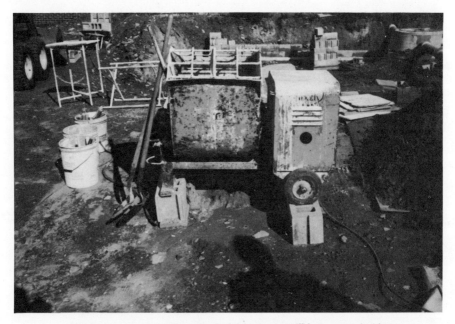

If you are using a small mechanical mixer, you will have an easier time mixing cement if you place the mixer on blocks as shown in the picture. Keep the mixer close to the sand pile. Always take the time at the end of the day to clean out the mixer thoroughly; it pays.

A mortar pan. The mortar pan is a worthwhile investment. You can use it to store the mortar while you clean the mixer. It can also be used for mixing mortar.

Ready Mix

In larger jobs around the home, you will save yourself a great deal of work if you use concrete delivered by a ready mix company. The advantages outweigh the extra cost of the ready mix. You don't have to borrow and take back a mixer. You don't have to worry about the possibility of error in the proportioning of the materials. You will also eliminate the time you would have spent finding sand and stone, and cleaning up after the operation.

Ready mix truck. These trucks are very heavy. Find out where your septic tank is and keep the truck clear of it.

There are some important things to remember when ordering ready mix concrete. The first is that the ready mix company is in the business of mixing and delivering concrete. It is not responsible in any way for the actual pouring or finishing of the concrete. You will find that although the driver will be able to give you some valuable help due to the fact that he sees concrete poured every day, he can't be expected to help screed, wheel, or carry the concrete. You should try to get some friends to help with the pouring. Ready mix prices vary from place to place, and in large cities you might be able to save 5 to 10 dollars per yard by contacting more than one company for pricing. Check in the yellow pages under "Concrete."

Another important thing to remember is that a concrete truck is very heavy even unloaded. Always check to see if the ground over which the concrete truck will pass will support the weight of a loaded truck. Be careful not to have them drive over a septic tank or well, or anywhere a heavy truck will damage the ground. Some companies state on their bill that they are responsible for delivery to the curbline only and the buyer assumes responsibility after that.

Forms for Concrete

Never order ready mix or start pouring your own mix until you are sure your forms will hold the weight.

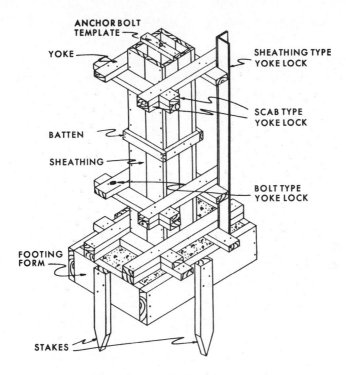

Form for a concrete column.

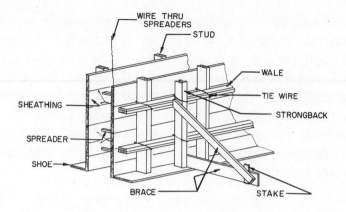

WIRE THRU
SPREADERS
STUD
WALE
TIE WIRE
STRONGBACK
SHEATHING
SPREADER
SHOE
BRACE
STAKE

Form for a concrete wall.

The forms should be well braced and at the correct height. Concrete is very heavy and causes pressure on the forms until it begins to set. Forms should be made of clear clean wood or metal. A piece of wood with a knot hole or splinters or bumps on it will show in reverse in the new concrete. It is common practice to use old oil on the form to make it easier to strip them after the concrete sets up. This also keeps the forms from drawing moisture from the concrete and causing it to dry out too fast. If you think you might want to paint

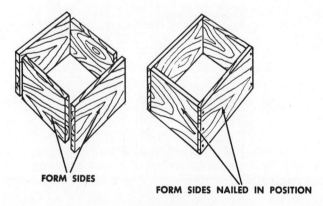

FORM SIDES

FORM SIDES NAILED IN POSITION

Small footing form.

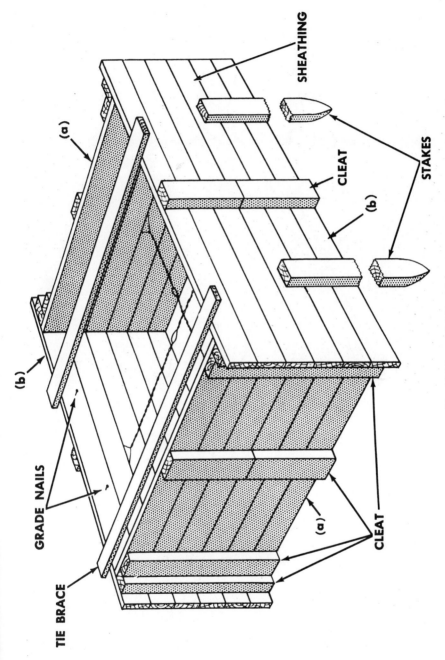

Typical large footing form.

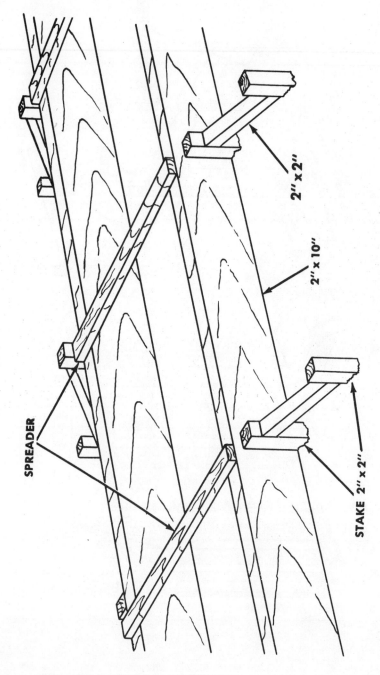

SPREADER

STAKE 2″ x 2″

2″ x 2″

2″ x 10″

Typical wall footing form.

the concrete at a later time, you should use water on the forms instead of oil, wetting the surface of the forms prior to pouring the concrete. Plywood is a good material to use for forms, as it is smoother and stronger than boards of the same thickness. Included in this book are some examples of forms, but most jobs require special designs because of different ground levels and dimensions.

Pouring and Placing Concrete

The pouring and placing of concrete should be done within 20 minutes after it has been mixed. This is because in warm weather with the sun shining on the

Pouring a footing. Notice how the forms are braced both across and with stakes on the side to keep them from lifting out of the ground. You may have to wheel some concrete to where the chute can't reach, so have a wheelbarrow handy.

poured concrete, the set up time will most likely begin in about 20 minutes. Try not to move or disturb the concrete once it has started to set in the forms since disturbing it will adversely affect its strength, especially along the edges. Never put water on poured concrete to remix it or to soften it. This will harm the surface causing problems after it cures.

To avoid what is called "honeycombing" — small and large holes that occur in the concrete where it sets against the forms — a machine called a "vibrator" is used. It has an electric motor and a long vibrating shaft that is placed in the form as the concrete is being poured. The vibration causes the fine aggregates and cement to fill the holes along the forms. If the job is small, you can vibrate the sides of the forms with a hammer.

Vibrator. The vibrator is used to consolidate the concrete as it is being poured. The action makes the concrete flow into every corner of the forms.

Try not to pour concrete into the forms from a height of more than two feet. Doing this can separate the aggregates causing the heavier stones to go to the bottom of the form. If you can find a coal chute, you are in luck; if not, make one out of three boards. When using a coal chute (or a chute you made yourself) hose it down before using it to make the concrete slide on it. When you finish, hose off the concrete before it has a chance to harden on the chute. All the tools used to pour your concrete should be washed as soon as possible. This will save a longer job of chopping off the hard concrete later.

Pour the concrete as near as possible to where it will finally be located. If you pull or push it around too much, you will seperate the aggregates and cause the

Concrete forms should be constructed of good straight lumber. Rough-cut lumber can be used, provided it is true (straight). Use reinforcing rods whenever possible, as it increases the tinsel strength of the concrete.

heavier stone to settle and the sand and cement to come to the surface, thereby causing poor wearability and glazing.

When pouring steps, brace the forms with stakes. Check and recheck all measurements before pouring the concrete. If the pour is big, have someone ready to help: once concrete starts to set, you can't stop it.

Bonding Old and New Concrete

Fresh concrete won't bond readily to old concrete unless the old is specially treated. When you pour new against untreated old, you usually have a crack as soon as the new concrete dries and shrinks slightly. Water can seep through this crack causing it to become larger as times goes on. There are ways to improve the bond between two pieces that are poured at different times. If the job requires that you stop pouring one day and then continue the next day, you can leave short rods or other steel protruding 12″ or more out of the center of the last poured section. Also, before removing the forms and before the last pour becomes hard you can make sure that the end has a rough texture. This can be done about two hours after you have poured the concrete.

A visit to your building supply dealer is advisable since there are bonding agents on the market that will keep the two pieces from cracking and leaking. Some of these bonding agents are made with a latex base and some with an epoxy base. Follow the instructions closely.

Tamper. Using a gas-engined tamper, you can tamp many times faster than by hand. Tamping the ground will give you much stronger floors.

Pouring in Cold Weather

If you plan to pour concrete in cold weather, you should use air-entrained Portland cement. When concrete freezes, the surface spalls (peels off). Air-entrained cement has tiny air bubbles that act as cushions to take up the freezing water in the concrete. Calcium chloride can be added at about 1½ pounds per 94 pound bag of Portland, to accelerate the setting time, enabling you to get your desired finish sooner. Concrete itself gives off a certain amount of heat through the chemical reaction which makes it hard. This is called "hydration."

The water used in mixing concrete can be heated as can the aggregates, though this would not be as practical in a large job.

High early strength cement is sometimes used in cold weather since it is richer and sets faster. You can obtain these same results by adding a larger proportion of Portland in your mix. Or you can use a smaller proportion of water. Remember to keep your proportions the same for each mix.

Finishing machine. This machine is used to float and finish the concrete, just by changing the blades. In large areas, the machine saves many hours of hand work.

Hot Weather Pouring

Hot weather causes problems too. Concrete will dry faster in warmer weather. The hotter the air is, the faster concrete sets. If the concrete is allowed to set too fast, it can dry crack and reduce the strength of the finished product. The best way to prevent drying out too fast is by the curing method used. As soon as the slab is hard enough for you to press on it with the end of a tool called the "float" without causing an impression, it is ready for the curing. Curing should be kept up for a few days. Curing is the retardation of the evaporation of the water from the concrete. Slowing down the evaporation can give you up to 33% stronger concrete. One way to cure effectively is to flood the slab with water. Remember to make sure the concrete has set before you flood the surface. Another way to cure the surface (especially if the work can't be flooded) is to use polyethylene sheeting. You can buy it in rolls or sheets. Put the polyethylene over the entire surface. This will hold the moisture in and slow the evaporation process. You can leave the forms in longer, keeping the sides covered. But as was explained before, oil the forms or put water on them before using them to prevent the forms from absorbing moisture from the concrete.

Reinforcing Concrete

Concrete can be reinforced by the addition of metal rods or bars. Reinforcing concrete increases the tensile strength. Tensile strength is the amount a given material can be stretched before it ruptures. To explain this in relation to concrete, we must understand that concrete has a great amount of compressive strength, but it does crack under strain. The addition of reinforcement increases concrete's ability to withstand twisting forces. The extra cost of reinforcing a footing against cracking is well worth it. If a footing cracks, the wall will also crack. Two ⅜ inch rods running an equal distance apart around the footing will be enough in small jobs.

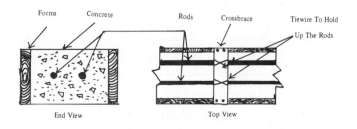

This cross section of a concrete slab shows the way the aggregates are spread throughout the concrete.

Curing Methods

Method	Advantage	Disadvantage
Sprinkling with water or covering with wet burlap.	Excellent results if constantly kept wet.	Likelihood of drying between sprinklings. Difficult on vertical walls.
Straw	Insulator in winter	Can dry out, blow away, or burn.
Moist earth	Cheap, but messy	Stains concrete. Can dry out. Removal problem.
Ponding on flat surfaces	Excellent results, maintains uniform temperature.	Requires considerable labor, undesirable in freezing weather.
Curing compounds	Easy to apply. Inexpensive	Sprayer needed. Inadequate coverage allows drying out. Film can be broken or tracked off before curing is completed. Unless pigmented, can allow concrete to get too hot.
Waterproof paper	Excellent protection, prevents drying.	Heavy cost can be excessive. Must be kept in rolls, storage and handling problem.
Plastic film	Absolutely watertight, excellent protection. Light and easy to handle.	Should be pigmented for heat protection. Requires reasonable care and tears must be patched. Must be weighed down to prevent blowing away.

The concrete buggy. These can be rented, and they are very handy if you have to pour far from the ready mix truck. The large wheels make wheeling easy.

When pouring a retaining wall, there should be drainage holes in the concrete. They should extend through to gravel on the back so that water can flow from behind the wall. This avoids a common problem with retaining walls: water pressure from behind.

Reinforcing wire should be put in concrete that will be exposed to the weather. It should be positioned in the middle of the slab. Here, half of the concrete was poured, the wire laid down, and the rest poured over the wire.

Tools and Equipment

Using the right tools and equipment always makes the job easier. This is especially true with concrete. If you make a list of the tools you will need, you will have them at hand when you start pouring the concrete. You won't want to leave the job to get a tool while pouring because concrete sets fast and if you leave it for a long period of time it will be hard to work when you return. On your list you might need most of the following tools or equipment. A wheelbarrow is handy to have even if you are making use of a ready mix delivery truck. You might want to pour some concrete where the chute on the truck can't reach, and you could wheel it to this area. A hoe, shovel, and a 5 gallon pail are needed if you are mixing your own cement in a wheelbarrow.

You will need a screed that is about 12″ longer than the width of your forms. Screeds are usually made out of 2″ × 4″ lumber. A screed is used to strike off or level the surface of the concrete with the top of the forms as it is poured. Before you decide to use a board as a screed, hold it up and sight down it to see if it is warped. If it is, it will either leave a crown in the concrete or a depression depending on which side of the screed is up. The correct way to use a screed is to pull it toward you in a sawing motion making sure you pull a small amount of concrete ahead of the screed to fill low spots. If you are going to pour a lot of concrete you might want to invest in a magnesium screed. It can't warp like wood or rust like steel, and it is light and easy to use.

The concrete should be screeded, usually with a 2″ × 4″ board. This will level the slab sufficiently so it can be floated and troweled.

If the slab is wide, you might have to stand in the middle of the forms to screed off the surface. Taking patience in screeding off the surface will make the finishing easier as the top of the slab will be smoother. You should always wear boots (they can be washed off later) and gloves to keep the wet concrete off your hands. The concrete can cause burns and if you get concrete in an open would it can cause an infection.

The first hand tool you will need is a float. As with most masonry tools, the float comes in many sizes and can be made of different materials. Here we see three different kinds.

This float made of magnesium is the longest-wearing, easy-to-work-with, hand float you can buy. Corners are rounded to prevent digging in. Either 12", 16", or 20" long and 3¼" wide.

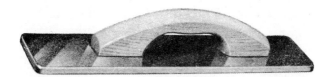

This plastic laminate float is moulded under high pressure. It wears like steel and works on the surface like wood. Its rounded corners help produces a fine finish.

Bevel edge redwood. Best for close form work. Made from select redwood, the edges are beveled to prevent splintering.

A float is used after the work has been screeded, to make sure the humps and low spots are smoothed out. It also brings the "fat" to the surface. The "fat" is the sand and cement that are brought to the surface by the action of floating. With no "fat" on the surface it would be difficult to fill in holes or voids. The float is held almost flat against the surface with a slight incline in the direction you are working. Press down and move the float in a 180° arc back and forth across the surface. You will find that you will be able to make the surface smooth but it will remain coarse and rough textured.

Some jobs require a rough textured surface. In barns or areas that animals walk, it provides a non-slip surface. On footings for block walls the top of the footing should be flat but not very smooth as the mortar will stick to a rough surface better. Float finishes are not recommended for exterior work as the surface won't wear as well. All exterior work should have a steel trowel finish.

If the surface of the slab is of considerable size, then it would be wise to either rent or build yourself a bullfloat. A bullfloat is made 6 to 8 inches wide and 42 to 60 inches long. There are four styles: Heavy duty magnesium, extruded magnesium, lightweight aluminum and laminated poplar. Below is a magnesium bullfloat and threaded handle.

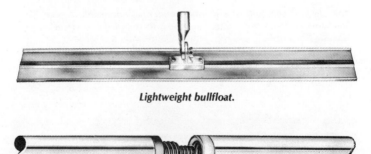

Lightweight bullfloat.

Long handles with positive locking molded threads.

Bullfloats have long handles with extra extensions for reaching across wide slabs and flattening the surface as soon after screeding as possible. It will make the troweling operation a lot easier. A bullfloat can be used on a slab right after it is poured since you will be standing next to the concrete and not on it.

Bullfloat. The bullfoat is used to smooth out any screed mark or humps you may have left in the concrete. By using the bullfloat you speed the finishing operation, because you are putting a partial finish on the concrete.

After screeding, the slab should be bullfloated. The bullfoat is pushed with the float raised so it won't dig into the slab.

After pushing, the bullfloat is drawn back across the slab with the edge raised so it doesn't dig in. Bullfloating smooths out a large number of humps and holes.

If possible, the slab should be bullfloated in the opposite direction than it was screeded, as shown here.

When pulling the screed back toward you, raise it slightly to avoid digging into the fresh cement.

Flattening the surface is best done as soon as possible after the screeding. It will make the troweling operation a lot easier. A bullfloat can be used on a slab right after it is poured since you will be standing next to the concrete and not in it.

A bullfloat can be homemade. If you have a 1 inch board that is about 6 to 8 inches wide and about 42 inches long, attach a handle to it, at an angle, so that you can push and pull it across the slab. The correct procedure for using a bullfloat is to raise the handle as you pull it across the slab and lower it as you push it across it.

For the final finishing of the surface, you should use a finishing trowel. Finishing trowels are made in a variety of sizes to suit a particular job. The most common finishing trowel for concrete work is 16 X 4 inches. It is made out of stainless steel.

The finishing trowel is used after the surface has been floated. You can usually tell when the surface is ready to be troweled. The sheen in the concrete will start to disappear and it will not leave much of an impression when pressed on with a trowel.

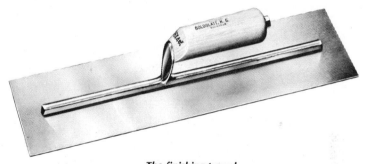

The finishing trowel.

The finishing trowel is used much the same way as the float. It is drawn across the slab in the same 180° arc as the float but with the trowel held at a steeper angle than the float. Each time you go over the surface

Edgers.

with a steel trowel you make it denser and harder and it is possible to obtain an almost glass-like surface finish. A ringing sound will be made when you have troweled the last time, because of the hard surface and the fact that no cement will be drawn in front of the trowel as you sweep it across the concrete.

If the concrete is to have any exposed edges, then you should use a tool to finish off the exposed edges. This tool is naturally called an edger. Below we see the curved end edger, the most used one. It has a stainless steel blade and is turned up at the edges for fast easy edging.

Hand edger. This jumbo (9" long, 4" wide) instrument is very easy to use and helps make the edge of the concrete slab last longer and look neater. The curved ends keep you from digging in when moving back and forth on the concrete.

Walking edger. This is the tool to use to avoid getting a sore back. The turned-up ends help prevent digging in. The 5' handle can be adjusted to the desired working angle.

The most commonly used edger is 6 inches long, and 3 inches wide with a ¼ inch radius. An edger is used to compress the concrete along the edges of the slab to keep it from spalling or being broken off. It also dresses up the finished slab.

Large slabs should have control joints in them to control the places where the slab might crack. Most slabs will crack due to shrinkage which occurs as the concrete sets up. A good rule to follow is to put a control joint every ten feet in either direction. More joints can be put in if you want to control cracks even further.

Control joints are made with a tool called a groover, the most common one being 6 inches long, and 3 inches wide with a ½ inch groove, and made out of stainless steel.

Walking groover. The groover is made of stainless steel and has all the edges turned up to prevent digging in. The walking groover is very helpful. You don't have to go out on a slab to make the finished joint, thus speeding up the work.

Groover. This groover for concrete is made of very durable material. The handle has a wing nut to allow you to work at a comfortable angle. Use the groover to put control joints in floors and walks.

The universal groover.

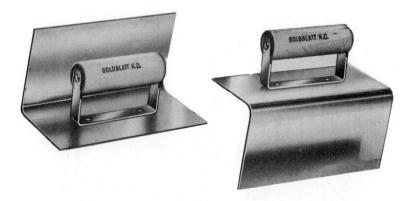

Step tools. These are matching inside and outside step tools for stairs requiring a batter. Both of these tools are 8" long and 4" wide with a ½" radius to give a ½" batter.

Custom step edgers. This tool comes in a matched set. It enables you to finish flush to either the right or left edge of the steps quickly and neatly.

A 45" mahogany darbie. This is a very useful tool for finishing concrete. After the concrete is screeded, the humps and low spots are fixed with a long darbie such as this one. The three hand holes make it easy to use. Work the concrete in a 180° arc with the tool raised slightly in the direction you are finishing.

The concrete rake. This rake is strong but lightweight, as it is made of magnesium. Concrete doesn't stick to it, and its weight and size (19½") make it valuable for moving concrete during the pouring process.

When working on the partially set-up concrete it is recommended that you borrow a pair of knee pads to eliminate sore knees and help yourself concentrate on the job at hand. The knee boards can be made out of a clean piece of plywood or a wide board. Make them about 12 X 18 inches, with a small piece of wood nailed to one end for a handle to pick it up with. Two knee boards are enough. One is used for your knees and one for your feet.

The purpose of knee boards is to allow you to get on the concrete to finish it before it gets too hard. Your weight is spread out by the knee boards and you leave a slight impression as you work the surface. If you make more than an impression of ¾ of an inch, get off the slab until it gets a little harder. Start the floating process in the same area as the pour started and finish in the same direction. If you come to a spot that is soft, work your way off the slab and wait for the area to get harder. If you make a very deep impression it can be hard to work out. Care should be taken when standing upright on the boards to avoid slipping and hurting yourself.

Sidewalks should be built at least three feet wide. A service walk may be made two feet wide. Forms should be made out of 2" by 4" lumber. The sides should be braced by driving in stakes deep enough to keep the sides from pushing out and tipping. Use a four foot level to check the forms. Compact the base so there won't be any movement to crack the concrete. The base should have a couple of inches of gravel leveled off so the walk will be four inches thick.

After the concrete has been poured into the forms, it is pushed and pulled with a rake or shovel until nearly level. It is then leveled with a screed. A sawing motion is used as the screed is pulled along.

After screeding the surface, a bullfloat is used to flatten the surface and remove any screed marks. A bullfloat will also bring finer materials to the surface to help with the finishing. The best way to use the bullfloat is to work in the opposite direction to that in which you screeded.

After bullfloating, the next operation involves using a hand float. The float is held against the surface with a slight amount of pressure. Move the float in a swinging arc, back and forth across the surface. Hold the edge of the float up slightly to avoid digging into the concrete. Keep floating until the surface is smooth and all the small holes are filled in.

Control joints can be made either by cutting them in with a jointing tool or by using an expansion joint material. This picture shows one way of using expansion joint material. The material is pushed into the concrete after it is bullfloated, at four foot intervals. Also shown in this picture is the finishing of the edge. This is done with an edging tool. The tool is flat with a rounded edge for compacting the edge and removing the sharp points. The edger can also be used in the expansion joint to dress it up. You will have better results if you use the edger after floating with the bullfloat and again after the hand floating. Don't press too hard on the edger.

After the pour has been finished, the surface should be covered with plastic or some other covering to promote curing. The bulkhead can be made out of the next piece of expansion material. Keep the walk covered for a few days.

Painting Concrete

The main thing to remember is that when you paint concrete, you must have a surface that is clean and free of dirt, salt, oil and other residue.

Before painting new concrete wait for it to cure properly. There may be moisture in the concrete that will bleed out and blister the paint.

Always rub the surface with a carborundum stone or something that will smooth the surface. This will remove any high spots or projections that might show in the finish. Fill the holes with a latex or epoxy filler to bond the patches to the concrete. Smooth out the patches after they dry and clean away any dust. All this preparation will result in a smoother wall, without imperfections, for painting.

The type of paint is up to the individual. The very best paint for the job has an epoxy base. If you use epoxy paint, you will have to mix the resin and catalyst together. This paint is more expensive, but it is also much more durable.

Before painting, use a heavy duty cleaner and a mildew wash on older concrete. If you want to prepare the surface even better, use an etcher.

3

PRECAST CONCRETE AND BLOCKMAKING

There are a lot of different precast concrete companies and they make a variety of concrete products. Precast concrete is made with forms and machines. The companies have the experience and knowledge and the right materials to construct precast products. The home handyman would find it very hard to duplicate these products, using hand tools.

Precast slabs of concrete for walks and patios save the handyman many hours of work and are less likely to break. A check with the local building supply dealer will show a variety of precast products. These might include splash block, parking curbs, chimney caps, benches, steps, and even septic tanks, to name just a few.

Concrete building blocks are actually precast concrete units. These concrete units are made in widths of 2, 4, 6, 8, 10, and 12 inches. They are made in either 16 or 18 inch lengths. The 16 inch length is most common. Some of the units are made in half high 4 inch sizes. Blocks are made in either concrete or lightweight materials. Most blocks are made with hollow cores, but they can be made solid.

The most common of the building blocks is the 8 inch block, which is actually 7⅝ by 7⅝ by 15⅝ inches long. The actual dimensions for other blocks are

Concrete septic tank and dry well. The tank and the dry well are very strong and will last a long time. In the top of each is an access door.

similar, 1⅝ for a 2 inch block and 3⅝ inches for a 4 inch block and so on. The reason for this is that when the blocks are laid in a wall with mortar, the dimensions (with a ⅜ inch joint) become 8 inches by 16 inches by.

The 8 inch block is made with either two or three cores, and weighs about 30 pounds. The 8 inch block is made in different forms for different uses, the most common being the stretcher. The stretcher has grooves and a concave center on each end. Corner blocks are made with a flat smooth end because the end shows on the outside of the wall. One other block is the "pier" block made with a flat smooth end on each end and is used for piers or when both ends of the block might be exposed, such as in a pilaster. Always check with the supplier to see if he might have any of these as they also make your work easier. Also make sure that when you are building something that has corners, you are ordering enough corner blocks. Some suppliers send every third block as a corner block.

Chimney Blocks

Chimney blocks are made in 16 × 16 and 16 × 20 inches, to accommodate flue liners of 8 × 8 and 8 × 13 inch sizes. These blocks are made in 7⅝ inches in height to allow for a ⅜ inch bed joint, but the outside dimensions of 16 × 16 and 16 × 20 vary greatly from manufacturer to manufacturer--sometimes by as much as an inch. If you are making an existing chimney longer check the outside dimensions before ordering more. The sides of all chimney blocks are smooth because they are usually exposed to view. Some chimney blocks are made with a hollow core in the block and some are solid, making them much heavier.

Special Colors and Sizes

Blocks are made in colors and special sizes, but only as special orders. Split block are actually solid block, with holes or without holes in them, which are snapped in two, lengthwise, exposing a rock-like texture on the face of the block.

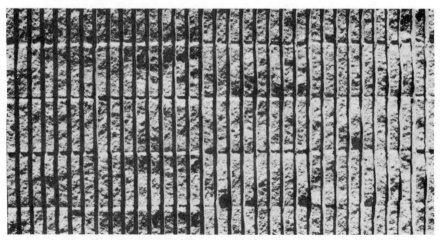

Split face blocks. These are solid with seven holes in the center. When split, they give the block a fluted appearance.

Screen Blocks

Screen blocks are made a little differently. They are made from white cement and white marble aggregate. These blocks have a fine smooth texture and sharp contours and can be used without painting. Any mortar or dirt that is splashed on the surface can be cleaned by lightly sanding and rinsing with water. These blocks are usually used for decoration but they can support loads just like other blocks. Screen blocks come in sizes of 11⅝ × 11⅝ inches and in widths of 3⅝, 5⅝, and 7⅝ inches.

Another use of the screen block is to hide an entranceway and support a roof. A close look will show how if they are used alone in a single course either vertically or horizontally they make one design, and if used in a wall show a series of circles. This wall also shows the concrete footing which is needed to hold the blocks up.

Screen blocks. These are usually stacked on top of each other without breaking the vertical joint. It is reinforced with thin rods of 4" "durwall."

Screen block wall.

Screen blocks used as a divider wall.

The back of the block making machine, showing the raw materials being pulled up a rail to be dropped into the hopper on top.

The front of the block machine. In the center of the picture you can see a chimney block being made. It will come out on a conveyer belt.

Concrete blocks are made by large machines out of coarse and fine aggregates and cement. Usually a machine can make one chimney block at a time but make four or six regular blocks at once.

Curing Blocks

After the blocks are made they have to be cured for a few days in the curing rooms. The curing dries the blocks and allows them to harden so they can be stacked awaiting use. Below we see the block that was just made coming out of the machine while in the foreground we can see two blocks coming from the drying room ready for use.

After the blocks are cured, they are stacked in what are called "cubes," so that a fork-lift truck can pick them up and load them on delivery trucks. Block

Cured and uncured blocks pass each other on conveyers.

The "green" blocks are arranged on drying racks before being placed in drying rooms. If you use blocks that are made by this process, you will find that all blocks are uniform in size.

delivery trucks can deliver blocks right to your foundation and place the cubes close to where you are working using a boom on top of the truck. These trucks and the loads they carry are very heavy, many times the weight of your car. Inspect the road they will take to deliver your materials to see if it will support the weight. If you have a spot near your work cleared out before the truck arrives, it can set the blocks close to the job and save you a lot of carrying.

You might want to deliver your own blocks to save the charge, but remember that the blocks are heavy and an automobile can't carry very many at one time. Be careful not to break your springs or your back.

The block delivery truck. These are heavy trucks, and you would be well advised to have the blocks delivered to save spraining your back. If you were to try to save money by picking up the blocks yourself, you would have to make twenty or more trips to handle what this truck can carry.

Keep All Material Dry

Once the materials are delivered, cover them if they won't all be used that day. This is true not only for blocks but also for cement and sand. Wet blocks lay a lot harder, even for an experienced mason. Sand can be deceiving when wet and you will likely get a soupy mix with wet sand. Cement can get hard if it gets damp.

Precast concrete steps are made in different heights and widths, with or without landings. They can be faced with brick or stone.

Precast steps are made hollow to save on weight, but they are still very heavy and require a strong base to support them. Consult with the supplier as to the weight and size base needed for each one.

An example of a precast step with a thin stone veneer and an iron railing. It is set on a concrete pad. Measure the width and the height you need and bring these dimensions to your dealer.

Common block now in use. From the left, 4", 6", 8", 10", and 12". Other sizes and shapes are available.

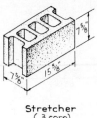

Stretcher
(3 core)

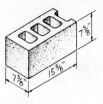

Corner

Double Corner or
Pier

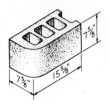

Bull Nose

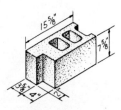

Jamb

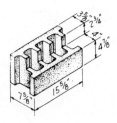

Full Cut Header

Typical sizes and shapes of concrete masonry units.

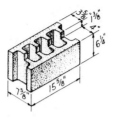

Half Cut Header

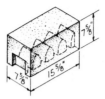

Solid Top

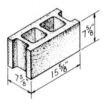

Stretcher
(2 core)

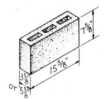

4"or 6" Partition

Beam or Lintel

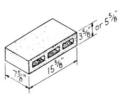

Floor

(Dimensions shown are actual unit sizes.
A 7⅝'' x 7⅝'' x 15⅝'' unit is commonly known
as an 8'' x 8'' x 16'' block.)

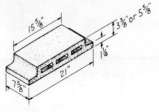

Soffit Floor

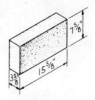

Solid

Solid Brick

Frogged Brick

Stretcher

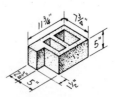

Jamb

Corner

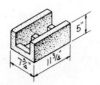

Trough

Partition

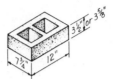

Stretcher

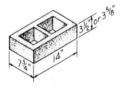

Corner

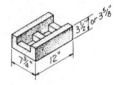

Channel

Stretcher

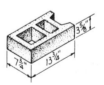

Corner

Channel

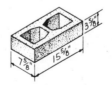

Stretcher
(Modular)

4

LAYING BLOCK

One of the biggest advantages of using blocks to build your project is that one man can do an entire project himself. Another advantage is that the work doesn't have to be done in one operation, as with concrete. The amateur can take as long as he likes to complete his project.

The first thing to do before you even dig a hole in the ground is to check with local building codes. You may be required to dig to a certain depth for your footing or be required to use a certain size block for a certain type of building. All of these factors will effect the cost of your project. It would be a costly thing to have to change something that didn't conform to the code. Some rural areas do not have building codes. Some areas have ordinances which are directed toward construction of buildings.

Try to design your project so it will have dimensions that are divisible by 8″. Doing this will save you material, since there will be less waste. You will also find that the practice of setting the measurements so they are divisible by 8″ will allow you to use whole and half units of masonry.

Before digging for the footing, find a point where you would like the top of the block wall to be when finished. Measure down in multiples of 8″ to ground level.

You should dig your hole down from here so it comes in block courses. An example would be: Your porch is 32″ off the ground and you want to add a set of steps. Dig another 24″ or 48″ (depending on depth frost goes in your area) and pour your footing 8″ thick. You will be able to lay block in 8″ high courses and come to the point you want on the porch.

For a block wall you need a poured concrete footing. The footing is usually made twice as wide as the block wall and at least 8″ thick. You can vary the width slightly but make it at least 8″ thick. You might be able to make the footing in the trench without using forms. You will need what is called grade stakes. Pouring concrete this way sometimes can be very difficult as it is easy to get humps and low spots in the footing. These humps can mean a lot of cutting to level the first course or alternatively a lot more mortar in the low spots. Therefore, it is always best, if possible, to use forms for your footing. An 2″ × 8″ on each side and a 1″ × 4″ for bracing.

Masonry blocks are laid much the same way as bricks. They should be laid in mortar joints of ⅜″ all the time to hold the dimensions of 8″ and 16″. Blocks should be kept dry until you are going to use them. Wet blocks slide in the mortar and sink so the joints squash out. Cover them with plastic until you use them. Wet blocks dry slowly.

One of the first steps is to locate the exact point you want for the corners of the wall. If your project is a large one and you have laid out batter boards as shown in the opening chapter, then you can drop a plumb bob down from the intersecting lines to locate the exact corner. Make a pencil mark here, or better yet drive a masonry nail in to keep from loosing the mark.

If your project is a small one, you can use a large square and lines from the corners to square the walls

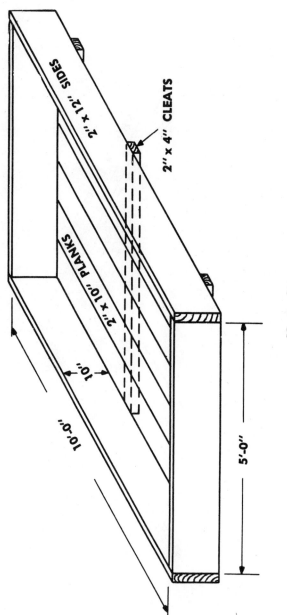

2" x 12" SIDES

2" x 4" CLEATS

2" x 10" PLANKS

1'0"

10'-0"

5'-0"

Mortar box

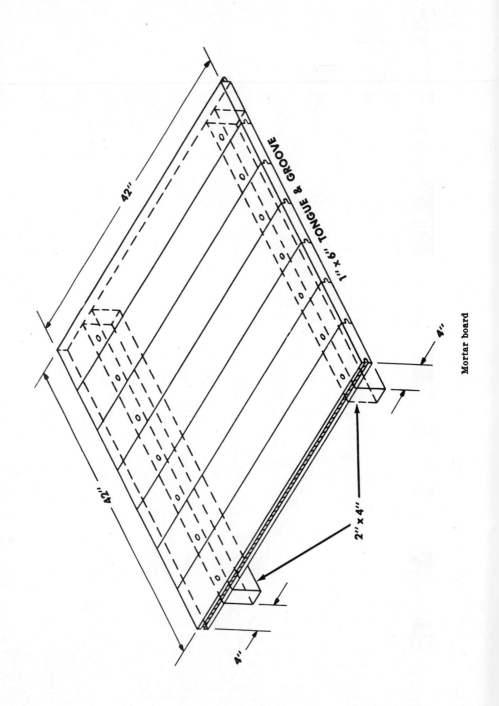

42"

42"

1" x 6" TONGUE & GROOVE

4"

4"

4"

2" x 4"

Mortar board

Place a nail in the footing at the exact corner. This will help you keep the point. A hard concrete nail works best. Measure to the next corner and mark the point. Do this around the footing. But before hammering nails into the other corners, check the diagonal measurements to make sure the building is square.

Lay a block dry at one corner and start making out the bond from this block. If you are using 16″ block, make a mark every 4′ until you get to the next corner. Place a block there in the direction it will be laid and continue laying out the bond around to the next corner.

If you can, use a "rod" to get your readings (height) at the corners. This is more accurate than a rule, which can bend and throw the reading off.

A tape measure that is frayed at the edge makes accurate measuring difficult. To overcome this problem have the tape held at the one-foot mark. This will give you an accurate reading, but don't forget to account for the extra foot.

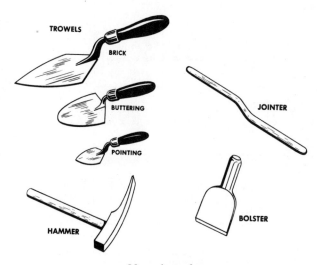

Mason's tools.

up. This is explained further in the chapter on laying out walls.

Mortar for block construction should be correctly mixed to bond well and provide a strong wall. The proportions you use in mixing the mortar will greatly effect its strength. Some walls should be made with a stronger mortar than others. The following is a suggestion of mortar mixes.

Type of work	Type of cement	Hydrated lime	Mason sand
Small ordinary jobs.	1 part masonry cement	none	2 parts
OR	1 part Portland cement	1 part	5 parts
Subject to heavy load or frost.	1 part masonry cement and 1 part Portland cement	none	5 parts
OR	1 part Portland cement	1/2 part	3 parts

Weights and Quantities of Materials for Concrete Masonry Walls

Actual unit sizes (width x height x length) in.	Nominal wall thickness in.	For 100 sq ft of wall			For 100 concrete units	
		Number of units	Average weight of finished wall lb*		Mortar** cu ft	Mortar*** cu ft
			Heavyweight aggregate lb*	Lightweight aggregate lb*		
3⅝ x 3⅝ x 15⅝ ------	4	225	3050	2150	13.5	6.0
5⅝ x 3⅝ x 15⅝ ------	6	225	4550	3050	13.5	6.0
7⅝ x 3⅝ x 15⅝ ------	8	225	5700	3700	13.5	6.0
3⅝ x 7⅝ x 15⅝ ------	4	112.5	2850	2050	8.5	7.5
5⅝ x 7⅝ x 15⅝ ------	6	112.5	4350	2950	8.5	7.5
7⅝ x 7⅝ x 15⅝ ------	8	112.5	5500	3600	8.5	7.5
11⅝ x 7⅝ x 15⅝ ------	12	112.5	7950	4900	8.5	7.5

Table based on ⅜-in. mortar joints.
*Actual weight within ± 7% of average weight.
**Actual weight within ± 17% of average weight.
***With face-shell mortar bedding. Mortar quantities include 10% allowance for waste.
Actual weight of 100 sq ft of wall can be computed by formula W (N) + 150 (M) where:
    W = actual weight of a single unit
    N = number of units for 100 sq ft of wall
    M = cu ft of mortar for 100 sq ft of wall

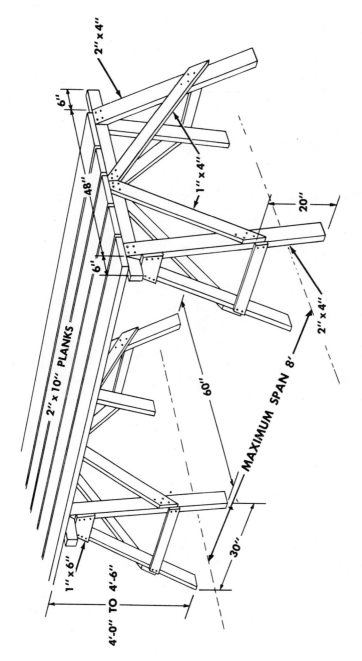

2" x 4"

6"

48"

6"

1" x 4"

20"

2" x 10" PLANKS

2" x 4"

60"

MAXIMUM SPAN 8'

1" x 6"

4'-0" TO 4'-6"

30"

Trestle scaffold.

Foot scaffold.

Make a Dry Run First

Start construction of your wall by making a dry run. Lay the blocks around the perimeter of the footing without using mortar. The reason for doing this is to allow you to space the blocks so they will all have a ⅜" mortar joint between them. You can do this with a rule or a piece of wood that is ⅜" thick. Mark the footing about every 4 feet with a lumber crayon, so that when you take the blocks away and start to lay them in mortar you will have something to go by. It is also a good idea to set up a chalk line from corner to corner lined up with the bottom of the blocks so that you can follow it as you lay the blocks.

Before you use mortar to lay your wall, first lay the blocks along the footing dry. You will be able to check the size of your joints, and you will be able to see if you have to cut any of the blocks.

WRONG

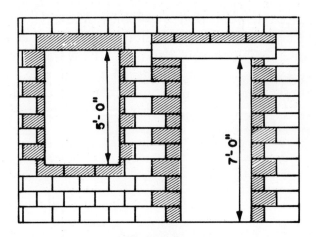

ELEVATION

SHADED PORTION INDICATES CUT MASONRY

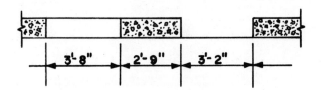

Planning concrete masonry wall openings.

RIGHT

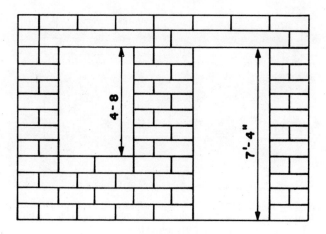

ELEVATION

ALL MASONRY FULL OR HALF SIZE UNITS

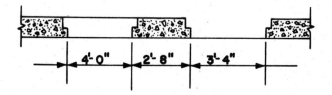

(BASED ON 8"x8"x16" BLOCK)

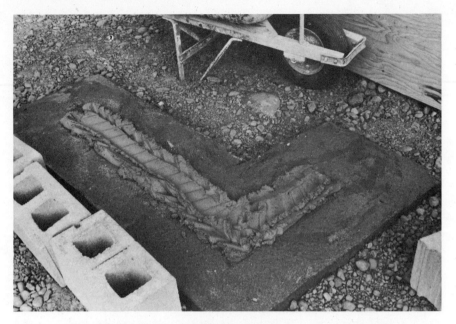

Spread the mortar out in a full bed joint for the first course of block. This will allow you to level and straighten the blocks more easily. It also gives the first course a better bond to the footing.

Spread the mortar on the footing as wide as the block and in a line long enough for at least three blocks. Use a corner block first at the exact corner. Place two more blocks against this in a line. Always lay the block with the thick side up. This side is made wider to provide extra room for the mortar.

Use a 48 inch long level to level the blocks from the corner blocks. If you start with the corner square and level, all the work that follows will be made much easier. The corner block should be laid 8″ off the level footing. If you're lucky enough to have an exactly level footing all around, you could lay all the blocks in the first course in 8″. This isn't always the case so you will have to start at one corner and lay it in 8″ and make the other corners come to that height. You might have to use a lot more mortar at one corner than at another but if you

Start laying your blocks from the corner. You should have a mark (a nail) in the footing at the exact corner. Lay the blocks in a bed of mortar and level them. Lay the first block at a height of 8 inches and level all the others from it.

Using the shorter (24") level, you should now be able to see if the wall is plumb. Hold the level against the side of the block and tap the block on top to plumb it.

start all the corners at the same height the wall should come out level. Use a shorter 24″ level if you have one, to check to see if the blocks are plumb. Plumb means straight up and down.

In fig. C we see the mason using the same level and hammer to plumb the other end of the first three blocks. After the ends are plumb, take a 48″ level, hold it as in fig. D and "range" the wall. This will make the middle block even with the ends and will also line up the blocks. Lay a couple of blocks off the corner in the direction of the next corner using the same operations and when you have done this get a large square and hold it against the side you leveled first, and square the second side with it as in fig. E. If you have a nail in the concrete at the other corners you can tie a line to it and range your corner from the line. Always range the wall from corner to corner on a big job.

C   *After plumbing the corner, go to the end of the first three blocks you laid to start the corner, and plumb the last block.*

D   *After you have plumbed the blocks, take your 48" level and "range" the wall. This is done to straighten the line of blocks and make the middle block the same as the others.*

E   *The next operation is to square the corner. Here, it is being done with a large metal square. If you can stretch a line to the next corner, you can hook it to the corner of these blocks and range your wall. Once you have lined up one side, use a square to line up the other.*

The Second Course

The second course on the corner should have the mortar spread on the sides of the first course as shown in fig. F. Be sure to put enough mortar on the blocks to hold up the next course. If you made the mortar so it is smooth and plastic, it will spread easier and will stick to the surface of the blocks better. Each course is laid in a similar manner. Make sure that you lay each block half bond over the one below it.

F   *For the second course, spread the mortar, as the picture shows, on each side of the top of the blocks. Use enough mortar to hold up the blocks. Good mortar spreads easily and sticks to the wall.*

G   *The blocks to be laid next should have their ends "buttered" (mortar spread on the ends). The ends should have enough mortar on them so there will be no holes in the joint when you lay the block in the wall.*

Buttering the Block

In fig. G we see the mason buttering the ends of the next block that is to be laid. This is the easiest way for the amateur to put a joint on the end of a block. A full end joint makes a much stronger wall. Press the mortar against the block as you spread it across the end of the block. Take your time doing this and you will find that it isn't hard to do. Once you have buttered the end of the next block you should be ready to lay it in the wall. Hold the buttered end up slightly as shown in fig. H and lower it into the bed joint and against the last block. Hold on to the block and let it go slowly into the mortar, preventing it from squashing the mortar out too fast. If your mortar is stiff enough it will hold the block up slightly allowing you to level it before it is low.

H   *When laying the block in the wall, lay it down into the bed joint and against the last block, as shown. This makes a better bond between units.*

Lay Up the Corners First

It is good practice to lay up the corners first and then stretch a mason's line from corner to corner to fill in the wall. A mason's line can be stretched so there is little sag in the center of the line and therefore a minimum of sag in the block wall. A good mason will sight along the line to see if it is sagging. If it is, they lay a block in the middle of the wall and put a "twig" or something similar to hold up the line in the middle. The "twig" is a metal line holder that has a slot in it to hold the line even with the top of the block.

One method of holding the line on the wall so that you can lay blocks is to attach a line holder at each corner. The line is wound around the holder and pulled tight from one corner to the next. This type of holder is adjustable and will fit 4,6,8,10, and 12 inch block.

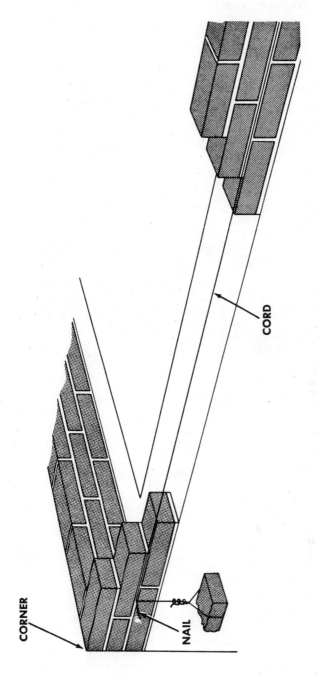

Use of the line.

Striking the Joints

Once the mortar is thumbprint hard, it is time to start to "joint up" or "strike up" the work. Use a jointer that is big enough to compact the joints without making a deep groove in the wall. Jointing a wall makes it stronger as you pack in the joint. It also helps make it weather resistant, and better looking.

Heavy duty convex jointers are the preferred tool for half-rounded or sunken joints. They come in 10½" lengths. Sizes available are ⅜" × ½" ½" × ⅝", ⅝" × ¾", ¾" × ⅞", and ⅞" × 1".

After the wall is built, you should install the anchor bolts to hold the building to the foundation. The anchor bolts are cemented into the foundation by using bolts that are bent at one end. Slide a board the size of the sill along as you set the bolts. This will enable you to get them set at the right height.

Once the mortar has gotten thumbprint hard, use a jointing tool to strike the joints. This compacts the mortar in the joint and makes a stronger and better-looking wall.

Some masons prefer to strike the vertical joint first, then the horizontal joint. Both should be struck, then floated and struck again.

After jointing, use a sponge rubber float and rub the wall, filling in holes in the block and broken corners. Go over the joints again lightly.

An optional operation is the method of floating the joints with a sponge rubber float. This dense float will smooth out the sharp projections left by the first jointing, and can also be used to fill in all the holes in the joints and any large chips in the corners. It is especially useful if you plan on painting the wall later. It is best to float across the joints in a circular motion since this won't pull the mortar out of the joints.

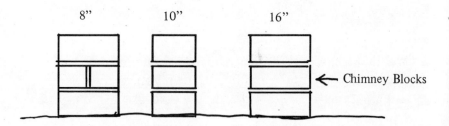

8" 10" 16" ← Chimney Blocks

Pilasters and Piers

Long walls can be strengthened with the addition of a pilaster. It is a good idea to use pilasters where the earth behind the wall is under pressure, as on the driveway side of the house where cars or trucks will be driven close to the wall or if you are building against the slope of a hillside. Some building codes require a pilaster every twenty or thirty feet. It would be wise to check the code if there is one. The following drawings show different ways to construct pilasters.

Pilaster in an 8" Block Wall

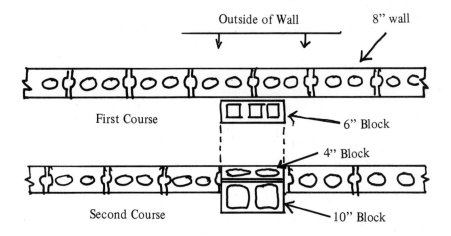

Outside of Wall   8" wall

First Course   6" Block

4" Block

Second Course   10" Block

In the above illustration, you see a pilaster in an 8" wall. If you were to build a 10" wall you would have to change the second course. You would use a 6" block in place of the 4" block.

Pilasters are built into walls to hold back pressure exerted against the walls. One way to construct a pilaster is shown here. One course of this 10" block wall shows a 6" block laid (centered on a joint of the 10" wall) against the 10" wall.

The second or next course shows a 6" block on the opposite side of the wall and a 10" jamb block on the top of the last 6". Laying the blocks this way ties the pilaster into the wall.

When constructing a pilaster in an 8" block wall, a 4" block is laid against the 8" wall, centered on a joint. The 4" block is cemented against the 8" wall.

On the second course the 4" block is laid on the 8" wall and an 8" jamb or square end block is laid over the 4". This ties the pilaster into the wall.

The effect of using the pilaster is that you have a built in brace against pressure exerted from the outside. If you were to place the pilaster on the outside of the wall it would have little or no effect against the pressure against the wall.

Piers are no more than stacking blocks on top of each other.

Brick piers should be filled in solid. This makes them more resistant to water damage. Old brick or block make excellent fill material. You will have to continually check the measurements to make sure the pier doesn't get bigger or smaller.

Six Inch Corners

If the wall you are building happens to be made out of 6″ block, you will have to construct the corner a little differently than if you were building with 8″ block. All the blocks are the same in length and in order to remain on what is called half-bond you have to cut the 6″ blocks that are used at the corner to 14″ long. Fig. K shows that when you cut the block to 14″ long the next block will come out half-bond. This is done for looks and to make the wall stronger since half-bond is the strongest bond.

When laying a wall using either 10″ or 12″ blocks you will have to purchase what is called corner blocks or L corners. If you look at figs. 4L and 4M you will see how this works.

A 6″ corner showing how a block is cut to 14″ long to keep the wall on half-bond.

When laying a wall using 10″ or 12″ block, it is necessary to use "L" corners to keep the wall on half-bond. This is the first course.

The second course in 10″ or 12″ block corners. Note how the "L" corner keeps the wall on half-bond.

Connecting one masonry wall to another can be accomplished by the following method. Lay a block against the wall at the intersecting point. If possible, it should be a full block. On the top of this course place a 2" wide 24" long piece of strap metal. The ends should be bent up on one end and down on the other.

The second course is laid over the strap metal and the holes in the block that are over the strap ends should be filled in solid with mortar.

If it isn't possible to lay up all the block walls at the same time, you might want to "tooth" the wall and fill in the wall later. As shown in the picture, lay a piece of block on the last course and spread mortar only on the top. (You will be able to remove it easier.)

After the work is finished for the day, the wall should be covered to keep moisture out of the wall. Wet blocks are hard to lay. The area at the bottom of the wall should be clean and the bottom joint made convex to allow a waterproof cement to curve onto the footing.

5

BRICKMAKING

Brick and tile are produced by mixing finely ground clay with water, forming it into the desired shape, then drying it and burning it. In ancient times, all molding was performed by hand. However, since the invention of brickmaking machines during the latter part of the 19th century, practically all structural clay products produced in the United States have been machine made.

The clay is crushed to break up large chunks and remove stones, after which hugh grinding wheels weighing 4 to 8 tons each revolve in a circular pan, grinding and mixing the material. Most plants then screen the clay, passing it through an inclined vibrating screen to control particle size.

Tempering, the first step in the forming process, produces a homogenous plastic mass ready for molding. This is most commonly achieved by adding water to the clay at the pug mill, a mixing chamber which contains one or two revolving shafts with blades. At the present time, there are three principle processes for forming brick and tile, the stiff mud, the soft mud and the dry press processes.

All structural tile and a large percentage of brick are produced by the stiff mud process. In the stiff mud process, clay is mixed with only enough water to produce plasticity, usually 12 to 15 percent by weight.

Stiff mud process. The mixture is forced through a die (at the right of the picture) along a belt to the cutter. The cutter revolves and cuts, making the bricks a uniform width.

After thorough mixing ("pugging"), the tempered clay goes through a de-airing machine in which a vacuum of 15-29 inches of mercury is maintained. De-airing removes air holes and bubbles, giving the clay increased workability and plasticity and resulting in greater strength.

Next the clay is forced through a die, after which it passes through an automatic cutter. Cutter-wire spacings and die sizes must be carefully calculated to compensate for normal shrinkage during wet stages and through drying and burning. As the clay column leaves the cutter, it is passed through a color adding hopper and a texture pressing roller.

The man in this picture is adding a coloring agent to the soft brick through a hopper. On the left a roller is creating a rough texture.

As the bricks move along, the belt inspectors remove the imperfect units and they are returned to the pug mill. The units that pass inspection are taken off the belt and placed on dryer cars. These cars are on tracks to make moving around the plant easier.

When the clay units come from the molding or cutting machines, they contain from 7 to 30 per cent moisture depending upon the forming method. Before the burning process begins, most of the water is evaporated in dryer kilns at temperatures ranging from about 100° to 400° F. Drying time, which varies with different clays, is usually from 24 to 48 hours. In all cases, heat and humidity must be carefully regulated to avoid excessive cracking.

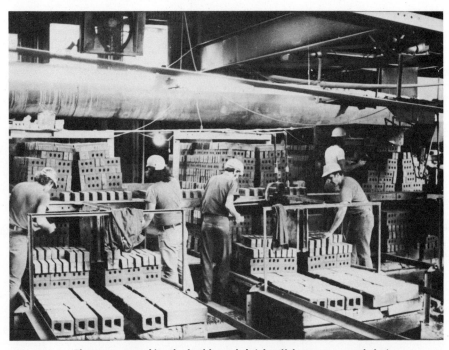

These men are taking the freshly made bricks off the conveyer and placing them on cars for drying and firing in the kiln. The brick must be stacked a certain way to be properly fired.

Loaded rail cars being pushed through the kiln tunnel.

Glazing is not common to all manufacturers, but it is an important operation in the production of facing tile, terra cotta and some brick. Ceramic glazing is a highly specialized, carefully controlled procedure, having two basic variations: high-fired and low-fired glazing. High-fired glazes are sprayed on units before or after drying and then kiln burned at normal firing temperatures. Low-fired glazes are used to obtain colors which cannot be produced at high temperatures. They are applied after the unit has been burned to maturity and cooled, then they are refired at relatively low temperatures. Spray glazes are composed of several mineral ingredients that fuse together in a glass-like coating at a given temperature. Glazes are available in almost any color.

The next step is burning. Burning is one of the most specialized steps in the manufacture of clay products, requiring from 40 to 150 hours, depending upon the kiln type and other factors. Several kilns are in use, the chief types being the tunnel and periodic kilns. Fuel may be natural gas, oil, or coal.

The dryer units are set in the kilns in a pattern that permits free circulation of hot kiln gases. In a tunnel kiln, units are loaded on special railroad cars which pass through various temperature zones as they travel through the tunnel.

The rate of temperature must be carefully controlled, depending on the raw material as well as the unit being produced. Kilns are equipped with recording pyrometers to provide a constant check of the firing

After the bricks are fired, they cool down. They are stacked by hand in cubes of 500.

Each cube of brick will have instructions on how to unload them to get the best variety of colors.

There are many different kinds of brick to choose from. Visit a yard and pick out the ones you like from piles of cubes of brick like these.

process. Near the end of the burning process, the units may be "flashed" to produce color variations.

After the temperature has reached the maximum, the cooling process begins. Forty-eight to seventy-two hours are required for proper cooling in periodic kilns. In tunnel kilns, the cooling seldom exceeds 48 hours. Because the rate of cooling has a direct effect on the color and because excessively rapid cooling will cause cracking and checking of the ware, cooling is an important stage in the burning process.

The next step is unloading the bricks from the rail cars and putting them in cubes of 500. There would be less in a cube of larger brick. All cubes have unloading instructions on how to get the best variety of colors.

6

BRICKLAYING

When the weather becomes warm in early spring, many homeowners begin turning their winter dream projects into real patios, barbecues, walkways and landscape edgings.

Most of these outdoor projects can be executed easily and inexpensively in brick. With 10,000 colors and textures available, you can choose brick that ranges from near white to almost black, from glassy smooth to rough. Brick prices range from five cents to eighteen cents each, depending on the selection, quantity, and area of the country.

Brick arrive at your dealer's yard on pallets or banded with straps in quantities of 500, and this is the most economical and efficient way to buy them. For an additional charge, your dealer will deliver the brick to your site, ready to be used when you are. You can, of course, buy brick by the hundred or a dozen at a time, but you are running the risk of breaking a few bricks, your car springs and your back.

Many Different Sizes Available

Among the more recent developments in the brick industry are the various sizes in which brick are now available. Experience has indicated that there are certain savings available with the selection of specific sizes of brick for various applications. Some of the larger

CHARACTERISTICS OF BRICK AND BRICK MASONRY

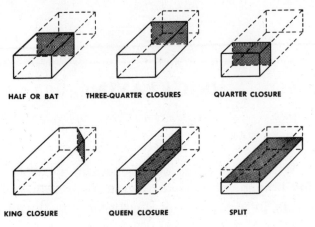

Shapes of cut brick.

brick offer savings in the laying out process, while some of the thinner brick offer savings in material costs. These savings can be very attractive.

Except for the non-modular standard, oversized and 3″ units, most bricks are produced in modular sizes. The nominal dimensions of modular brick are equal to the manufactured dimensions plus the thickness of the mortar joint for which the unit was designed. In general, the joint thicknesses used with brick are either ⅜″ or ½″.

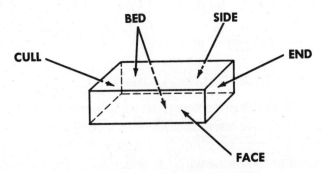

Names of brick surfaces.

The actual manufactured dimensions of the units may vary, of course, from the specified dimensions. It should be noted that the designated manufactured heights for the standard brick, the standard modular brick and all other modular brick designed to be laid three courses to 8″ are the same (2¼″).

Getting Started

For all but the simplest projects, your first step should always be to check local building codes. This will tell you, for example, how deep the concrete footing for your project will be, which will affect your brick estimate. Don't rely on second hand information about building codes requirements; it's no fun to find out that the concrete base for your wall should have been deeper after you've already finished it.

Discuss the location of your project with the family. For example: you might want the sandbox within sight of the kitchen. In most areas of the country, SW brick (severe weathering brick) are recommended for outdoor projects. Your building supply dealer can guide you in your choice of an appropriate and appealing brick.

Brick is made in many different sizes, but most outdoor projects can be planned and built with standard brick units. These measure 3¾″ × 2¼″ × 8″, and weigh about four pounds. Laid flat on sand, each brick of this size will cover 30 square inches. A pallet of brick (500) on sand will cover about 100 square feet, or enough for a 10′ × 10′ patio. If you lay 500 of these brick flat in a mortar bed with ½″ joints, you'll be able to cover nearly 120 square feet, or enough for a 10′ by 12′ patio.

If you're planning a barbecue, you'll need to figure from your plan the square footage of surface on the walls and chimney. Multiply the total square footage by

7 if your walls and chimney are one brick wide. If they're double width, multiply by 14. For brick counter tops, multiply the square footage by 4½.

Lawn edgings are simple. Multiply the length of the edging by 12 to get the length in inches, and divide that number by the width of your brick. If you need 100 feet of edging to surround your home, you'll need 320 standard bricks ($100 \times 12 = 1200 \div 3\frac{3}{4} = 300$).

A mason will carry upwards of thirty different tools with him to do different phases of the bricklaying job. You should be able to do most of the jobs around home with the following tools:

Level. Used to level the work and also to keep it straight up and down (plumb).

Hammer. The mason's hammer is different from the common claw hammer found around most homes in that it has a chisel shape side and a hammer side. You might be able to get along without the mason's hammer if you have a brick chisel.

Brick Chisel. The brick chisel is about 4″ wide and is used to cut brick and block to length.

Rule. This is not just any rule, but a folding wooden rule so it can be held in one hand while you mark spaces with your free hand.

Trowel. If you are doing a one and only repair or a remodeling job, then you can get away using a cheap trowel. But, if you intend to do many home projects, then buy a good quality trowel since this is the tool you will have in your hand from the word "go" to the word "finished."

Convex Jointer. The jointer is used to finish off work and compact the joints thus making the work stronger. It is a good tool to have. The best one to buy would be one with a ⅝ × ½″ width.

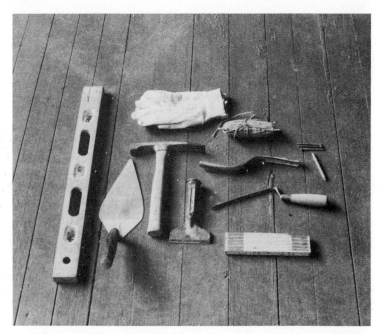

The tools needed to build a brick or block wall. From the left: a 24" level, trowel, mason's hammer, brick chisel, mason's line, jointer, tuck pointer, and rule. Also gloves, nails, and a pencil.

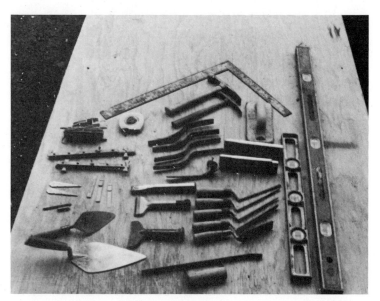

A mason might carry all these tools with him to enable him to do many different projects. It would not be worthwhile for the homeowner to own all these if he did not use them frequently.

Mason's Line. A good mason's line is handy since you can pull it very tightly without it breaking. It is thin and used to guide the work from one end of the wall to the other. Line blocks or pins will hold the line secure at each end.

Preparing the Site

Many projects work best over a level concrete base. Excavate to the depth required by the local building code, and prepare the quantity of concrete needed. Allow the concrete to season before starting to build on it. Usually a few days to a week is enough.

A level, stable site is particularly important for mortarless projects. Many of these, such as patios and walkways, can be laid over sand and gravel instead of concrete.

Estimating Sand and Gravel

In mortarless projects, the amount of square feet that a ton of sand will cover is shown in the following chart.

	SQUARE FEET PER TON IF SPREAD		
	1" thick	2" thick	4" thick
Sand	276	138	69
Gravel	229	116	58

Essentials of Good Workmanship

Mortar cement is different from Portland cement and is made for laying masonry units. It should never be used for footings or in place of Portland cement.

Mix as much mortar as you think you will use in one or two hours. It should have the consistency of soft mud. If it begins to stiffen, temper it with a small amount of water. For a large project you might want to rent a mixer since mixing mortar fully will result in a stronger wall. A mortar mixer is different from a concrete mixer in that a mortar mixer has a drum that has paddles revolving around inside it. The concrete mixer drum has stationary paddles and the whole drum revolves. Aggregates in the mix help mix the concrete.

There are two ways to obtain mortar. The easiest way is to buy a sack of dry-mix mortar, add water, mix and you are ready for the trowel. One sack of dry-mix is enough for about 40 bricks.

While dry-mix isn't expensive, it does cost more than the mortar you make yourself out of the raw materials cement and sand. Enough cement for 40 bricks can be made from 1½ shovels of mortar cement and 4 shovels of sand. Mason sand is finer than concrete sand and would require more cement if used for concrete work. A much coarser sand is used in concrete. You may use Portland cement in place of masonry cement if you add hydrated lime. Mix one shovel of Portland cement with ¼ shovel of hydrated lime and 4 shovels of sand. In both mortar cement and Portland-lime mix you put sand in the mixer first then add the cement. This will prevent the cement from caking on the sides of the mixer.

Mixing in a Wheelbarrow

If you decide to mix in a wheelbarrow, you will need a hoe, a shovel and a pail. A hoe with holes made for mixing cement stirs the cement better, and more easily.

Measure the Amount of Materials

If you are mixing many batches of mortar and you want to be able to keep all the mixes alike, measure the amounts. Use different size pails or just one and make some sort of mark on the side of the pail so you won't lose count of the number of shovels or the quan-

The equipment needed for mixing in a wheelbarrow. In the background is a mortar pan, and against the 5 cubic foot wheelbarrow, a mortar board.

Adding water to the mix. Note the furrow to hold the water as mixing begins. Measuring amounts saves time and trouble.

tity of water needed. It is very easy to add just a little but more water, but if you put in too much you will have to figure out small proportions of sand and water to make it workable again. Soupy mortar is wasted very easily.

When mixing in a wheelbarrow you should combine the sand and cement together until the mix is a uniform gray color. Make a furrow in the center of the wheelbarrow. Pour in about half of the required amount of water. Mix this up slowly; it will be difficult at first. Keep adding the rest of the water slowly until you have it mixed up completely.

A Quick and Easy Check

After the mortar is mixed in the wheelbarrow you can make a simple test to see if it is workable and mixed properly. Take your trowel and pick up a trowel full of mortar. Shake the trowel with an up and then down flick of your wrist. Turn the trowel over. The mortar should stick to the trowel. If this is so, when you are using the mortar, it will stick to the vertical sides of the masonry. If your mix is soupy you can add sand and cement in a two to one proportion to stiffen it up.

Cement that is mixed properly will stick to your trowel.

As the mix drys out in the first hour or so, it may be tempered with water to improve its workability. Tempering is no more than sprinkling a small amount of water over the surface and working the mix around. After 1½ to 2 hours, the mortar will have started to set up in the chemical reaction called hydration, and it should not be retempered. If possible, you can throw the old mortar in the middle of the wall or in some holes that will have to be filled later with mortar anyhow.

Mortar will remain in usable condition longest on days that are cool, damp, cloudy, or with little wind. It will set faster on hot, dry, windy days, so it is a good practice to keep the mortar covered when not being used. Only wet mortar (as wet as is practical to use) will develop a good bond with bricks and blocks, especially the kind that are highly porous. Most defects in masonry result from poor bond between the units being cemented together. Dry, no-bond cracks allow water to pass into a wall and result in subsequent cracking of the wall. When masonry bonds correctly together it makes a more water repellent wall. This is also due to correct proportions in the mix and good tooling of the joints.

Joints that are small or tight are better than wide joints. Full end joints, level and full bed joints and properly constructed walls are less likely to leak.

Laying Out the Wall

Before laying a brick wall in mortar, begin by laying out the brick dry around the perimeter. This will allow you to space each one so you will have a ⅜" joint between them. Always start at a corner with a full brick, putting a cut if you happen to have one against an inside corner or old wall. The main purpose of laying out a wall is to get rid of any cuts if it is possible. When building a three or four sided building you can usually lay the brick around the perimeter and adjust the joints to remove a cut or "bat" in the wall. One way to remove a cut in the wall is to change to ½″ joints for a distance along the wall. In just 6 feet you can make up 1⅛″. Never make the joints larger than ½″; the strength or your work will suffer.

For the sake of a good looking wall, you should keep the bed joints about the same thickness as the end joints. Dark color brick will make your joints show up more and if you had many different size joints or a large joint in the middle of many small ones it would detract from the looks of the wall. This is the reason that masons use what is called brick spacing rules or a modular rule that allows brick to be laid three courses to eight inches.

Always lay the first course out dry. This allows for adjustment of the joints. Always start with a full (whole) brick on a corner.

Correct way to hold a trowel.

Proper way to hold a brick.

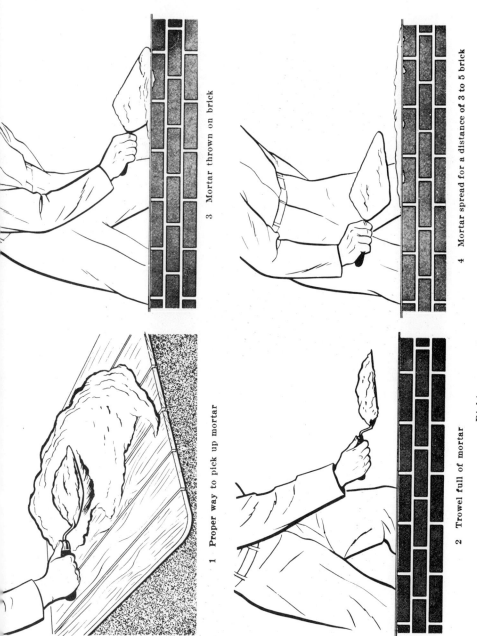

1 Proper way to pick up mortar

2 Trowel full of mortar

3 Mortar thrown on brick

4 Mortar spread for a distance of 3 to 5 brick

Picking up and spreading mortar.

Step 1

Step 2

Step 3

Bed joint and furrow.

Step 1

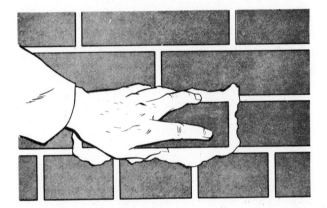

Step 2

Step 3

Laying inside brick.

Full Joints Make a Difference

Spread the mortar on the footing just slightly thicker than the bed joint should be, as this will allow you to adjust the brick in the bed joint until it is in its final position.

Spread enough mortar for about three bricks. The mortar should stay soft until you have laid the bricks. However some bricks absorb moisture faster than others and you might want to experiment to see how far along the bed you can spread the mortar.

Lay the first brick on the corner, then butter the end of the next brick you will lay. Press the brick down into the bed joint and against the last brick at the same time forming a bond between them.

Lay the brick in a full bed of mortar. A full end joint makes a stronger wall.

Put a small amount of mortar on your trowel and butter the end of the brick. Press the brick into the bed joint against the last brick.

After the brick is buttered, place it in the bed joint and, at the same time, against the last brick, forming the bond between the two bricks. Hold the brick between your thumb and fingers and rock it into place as you push it down.

When you have rocked the brick into place, take your trowel and remove the excess mortar to see how the brick looks. Now you can tap it lightly into final position with the trowel.

Using a short level, check to see if the bricks are level. Tap them lightly, and if they are low, pick them up and re-lay them.

After leveling the bricks, plumb each end, as shown here, with the short level held in the upright position. Tap into position.

Use a short level to range the bricks between the ends.

Rock the Brick Into Place

When you lay the brick in the bed joint, the easiest way to hold it is to position one side with your thumb and the other with two fingers. Push down lightly and at the same time against the last brick. As you are pushing down, rock the brick slightly to move it out to the edge or back away as shown. When you have rocked it down to the line or to a point where you will put your level on it (if you are building a corner you will be using a level not a line as shown) cut the excess mortar off the joint. At this point you can see if the brick is in its proper position.

Don't try to lay the bricks out and then cram mortar in between them into the joints; you will be moving bricks all over the place and will not have a structurally strong wall. In the process, you might leave voids where water could collect and start a crack.

Once you have laid three bricks from the corner you will next check to see if they are level. Check the thickness of your joint, and try to make them all the same size. A mason's rule will help mark off heights.

After you have leveled the brick and checked the height, you should hold the level in the plumb position (up and down) and check to see if the bricks on each end are plumb. Tap them on the top lightly as shown.

After you have used the level to level and plumb the corner you then can hold it in a sideways position against the wall and straighten any bricks between the two end bricks. Doing this is called ranging.

After the mortar has become thumbprint hard, you should begin the jointing up. A concave jointer will compress the joints and make a stronger and better looking wall as shown. Another way of finishing a wall is with raked joints.

Concave jointing.

If you decide to use raked joints, use the joint raking tool as shown, raking out first the vertical and then the horizontal joints. The joint raker has a nail for a point, and it can be adjusted to regulate the depth to which the joint is raked.

When laying brick using a raked joint, first rake out the mortar in the end joints. Make sure the wing nut holding the nail in the rake jointer is tight. Uniform depth of the joint is very important.

Next, rake out the bed joints. If you lay a lot of bricks, leave the last course each time (don't joint it) until the end of the work day. You might otherwise disturb the set or move the bricks on the last course.

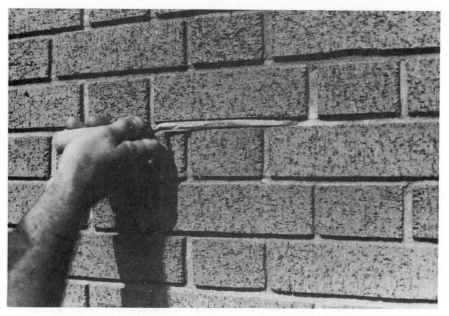

After the joints are raked, use a tuck pointer to smooth the raked joint and to compact the mortar in the joint to help make it water resistant and stronger.

Some jobs call for only the bed joint to be raked out. Make sure you have full end joints when laying the brick. This will make the work easier.

Bonds and Joints

If you look closely at many different brick walls, you will notice that the walls are made more beautiful and interesting through the use of different and appropriate "bonds." When we say "bond" we mean the pattern in which the bricklayer laid the brick in the wall. Bonds add to the strength of a wall or infrequently make a wall weaker. The bond that is the strongest is the running bond. A running bond may be with struck joints or with raked joints or with flush joints. All the vertical joints are staggered at half bond, meaning half way over the brick below. The next bond is the common bond. It is a variation of the running bond with a course of "headers" (end of the brick) at regular intervals — usually every sixth course tying the wall together.

"Stack" bond is created by using all stretchers or all headers and aligning them vertically. Stack bond is usually used only in veneered work or other nonstructural work. "Flemish" bond is a bond that is often seen in buildings of Colonial American design. It is made by alternating the headers and the stretchers with the headers centered over the stretchers above and below. "Screen wall" bond is used in a wall to leave an opening for air flow and for building structures to hide installations. Screen wall bonds use what is called ¼ bond, that is, ¼ of each brick is bonded to the next.

Types of joints and bonds can be left up to the individual who is building his own wall, as "beauty is in the eye of the beholder" as the saying goes and why not build it so you like the looks of it.

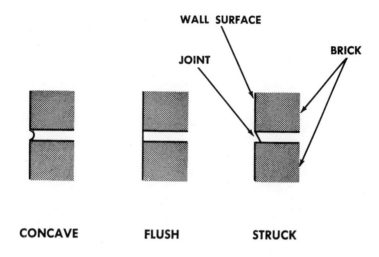

CONCAVE **FLUSH** **STRUCK**

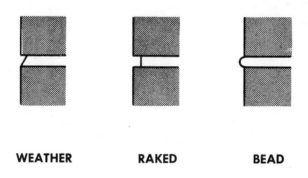

WEATHER **RAKED** **BEAD**

Joint finishes.

Cutting brick with a bolster.

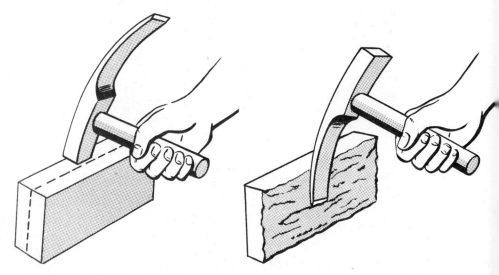

1   Striking brick to one side of cutting line   2   Trimming rough spots

Cutting brick with a hammer.

Head joint in a stretcher course.

Step 1

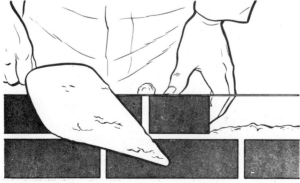

Step 2

Making cross joints in header courses.

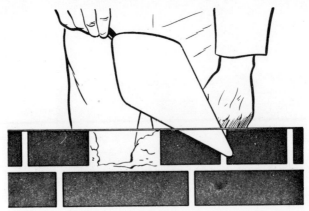

Step 1

Step 2

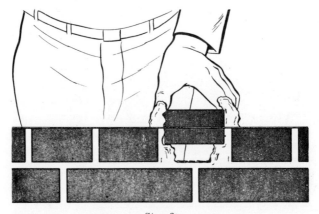

Step 3

Making closure joints in header courses.

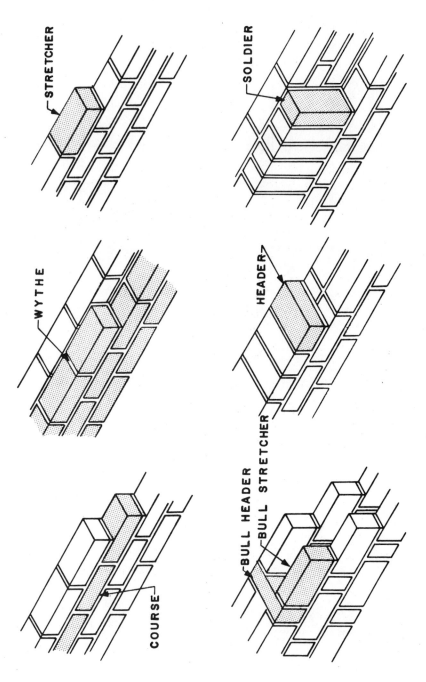

STRETCHER

SOLDIER

WYTHE

HEADER

COURSE

BULL HEADER

BULL STRETCHER

Masonry units and mortar joints.

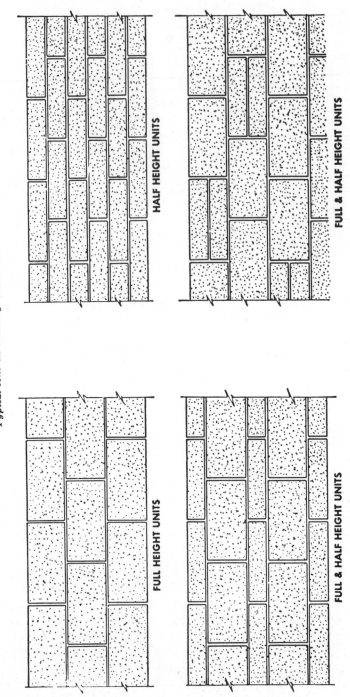

Typical concrete-masonry-unit bonds.

HALF HEIGHT UNITS

FULL & HALF HEIGHT UNITS

FULL HEIGHT UNITS

FULL & HALF HEIGHT UNITS

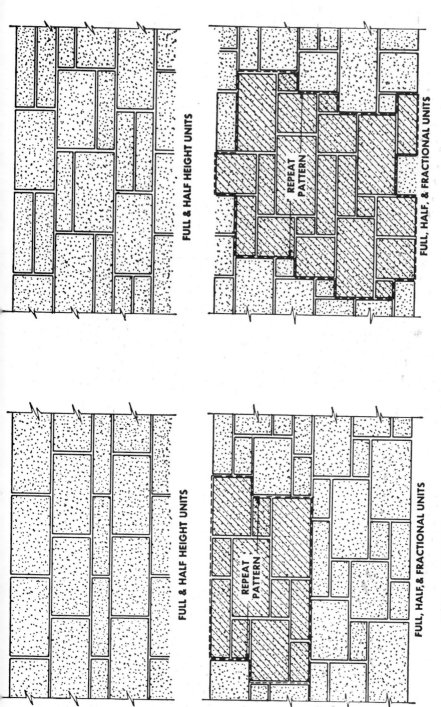

FULL & HALF HEIGHT UNITS

FULL, HALF, & FRACTIONAL UNITS

REPEAT PATTERN

FULL & HALF HEIGHT UNITS

FULL, HALF, & FRACTIONAL UNITS

REPEAT PATTERN

NOTE: ABOVE PATTERNS CAN BE PRODUCED WITH STANDARD UNITS—8″ x 16″ FACE, 5″ x 12″ FACE, AND 3¾″ x 12″ FACE IN USUAL WALL THICKNESSES. MANY OTHER PATTERNS MAY BE WORKED OUT BY THE ARCHITECT.

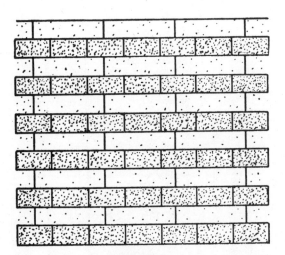

STRETCHERS, ABOUT 2¼" x 8"
HEADERS, ABOUT 2¼" x 3¾"
JOINTS, ABOUT ½"

COMMON

ENGLISH
(ALTERNATE COURSES OF HEADERS AND STRETCHERS)

Typical brick bonds.

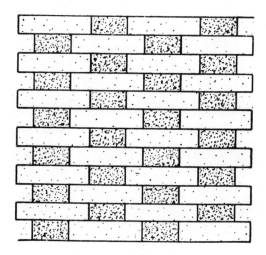

FLEMISH
(ALTERNATE HEADERS AND STRETCHERS)

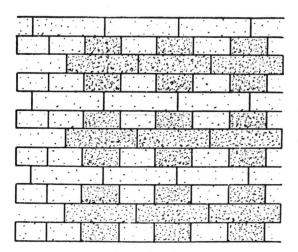

CROSS OR DUTCH

Struck joint. This wall is about 80 years old. The joints were struck with the mason's trowel as he worked. The struck joint is the reverse of the weathered joint, and it is inferior to the weathered joint because it doesn't shed water as well.

The rough cut, or flush, joint is the simplest joint. It is made by holding the edge of the trowel flat against the brick and cutting in any direction.

Running bond. This running bond wall has the joints raked out for effect. A running bond is one of the most commonly used, because of its strength.

Common bond. This is a variation of the running bond. It has a course of "headers" (brick laid with the short end along the face of the wall) at regular intervals. These headers may be used every sixth course tying in the brick wall with a block wall back up.

Stack bond. This is created by using all stretchers (as pictured), or all headers, and aligning all the vertical joints. Stack bond is usually only used in veneered work or other nonstructural work.

Flemish bond. This handsome bond is often seen in Colonial American buildings. Each course is made by alternating stretchers and headers. The headers are centered over the stretchers above and below.

Running bond with a soldier course. A soldier course is made by standing the brick up in the bed joint. This is a difficult bond for the amateur.

The screen wall. This type of wall is built to hide trash cans or other installations you want out of sight. The wall allows air circulation but also gives you privacy.

Combination of Flemish bond and running bond in the same wall. The Flemish bond is done in rough cut joints and the bricks are large, antique white, while the stretchers are made with concave joints done with a jointer. The bricks are also white, but a more common size.

Brick can be laid in many combinations. These are called bonds. The photo shows Flemish bond, with the end of the bricks (headers) sticking out slightly, making a shadow effect.

Shown here is jumbo or utility brick. The bricks are 4" × 4" × 12" and can be laid with a block wall. Two of these bricks are the same height as one block.

Weeping joints. These joints are made possible by allowing the mortar to be squeezed out from beneath the bricks and not jointing them. Some people consider this attractive, but it isn't weatherproof.

There are some modern buildings with unusual patterns. Here are the stack bond soldier courses and a corbelled out column. Brick factories make special brick for different applications. They do have to be specially ordered in large quantities, however.

Some block companies make a shadow block that can be laid in a diamond pattern, as is shown here. These blocks are 4″ thick and are held on the other 8″ wall by wall ties.

Types of Brick Walls

There are many kinds of brick walls, but only three need concern the homeowner.

The most common is the veneered wall, with facing brick placed outside the frame of the house and attached to the house by means of wall ties every two feet in each direction.

One other type of wall used in houses is the solid masonry bearing wall, which means that the wall carries the weight of the house. With this type of wall, there usually isn't a frame of wood behind the wall. Instead the brick and usually the "back-up" of hollow masonry units provide both enclosure and structural systems.

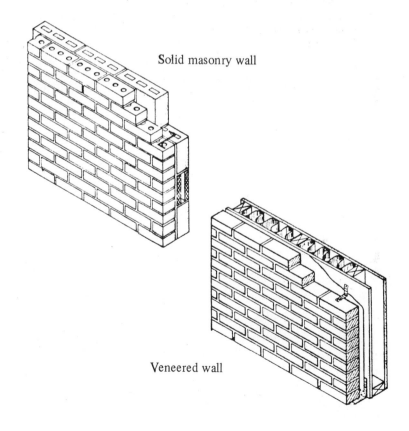

Solid masonry wall

Veneered wall

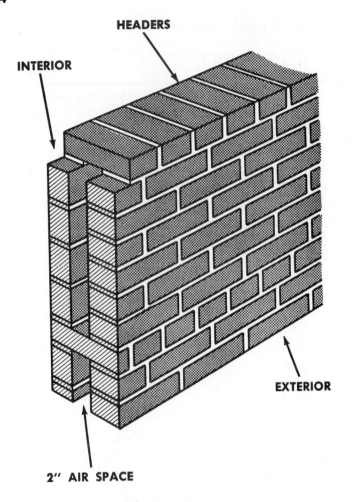

HEADERS

INTERIOR

EXTERIOR

2" AIR SPACE

Cavity wall

In some cases, a house may have a "cavity wall" (which is frequently a bearing wall also). This is a wall in which space is left between the outer and inner walls. However, exposed interior walls can be constructed inside a veneered or a solid masonry wall.

In townhouses brick walls frequently serve as bearing walls, supporting the weight of the structure. In addition, "party" walls which separate one townhouse from another also serve as a sound control as well as fire protection.

7

REINFORCING AND WATERPROOFING WALLS

Reinforcement of Walls

Walls that are close to a railroad track or some other place where there is strong vibration, or walls where there is questionable soil should have reinforcement built into them. Reinforcement is sold for block walls in the form of wire that lays in the bed joint when the wall is being constructed. It is made for different size widths of block. It is best when put into the bed joint as it is needed. This type of reinforcement helps to keep the wall from cracking.

Steel rods of different sizes can be placed vertically in a wall and the cores where they are placed can be filled with concrete or left over mortar. If these are filled solid they will help strengthen the wall against pressure from the side.

It is a good idea to use rods in a wall that is built against a hill that slopes toward the wall. If cost were no object, you could start with rods protruding from the concrete footing at two foot intervals and continued to the top of the wall.

Wait Before You Backfill

A foundation wall can be pushed over accidentally if it is not braced on the inside. New walls are called "green" until they have had a chance to harden completely. All block walls will have ability to hold weight, but they all are weak when it comes to being easy to knock over. Once weight is on the wall, its horizontal strength is greatly increased, and the likelihood of being pushed over is almost gone. On a new foundation, it is advisable to brace the walls. The illustration shows how a new wall can be braced. If possible, put the new floor on before backfilling. Have the operator backfill slowly and carefully so the wall won't have to be rebuilt.

After you finish the wall, brace the inside to prevent it from being pushed over when it is backfilled.

Waterproofing and Damproofing

Waterproofing and damproofing are best and least expensive when done during the initial construction of the building.

In places where soil has only a small amount of water, or where the drainage around the foundation doesn't let the water in the soil build up pressure, it is usually enough just to damproof the exterior of the foundation by applying two coats of coal tar.

A better method of damproofing is to apply two coats of cement mortar, each ½" thick, before applying the tar. The mortar should be 1 part Portland cement and 3 parts sand by volume. You can use ⅔ part cement and ⅓ part lime to make the mix set faster and if

The completed foundation. It has a cement coating and a coating of asphalt to waterproof the wall. The waterproofing should extend down and over the footing, with a drain tile around the perimeter.

you mix one cubic foot of mortar you should have enough to cover about 32 square feet of wall.

Before you coat the foundation with cement mortar, remove all dirt and loose pieces of cement. Then moisten the wall with water, not sopping wet, just enough to make the mortar stick better and to keep the wall from absorbing the moisture from the cement and allowing it to crack.

To insure a complete cover on the foundation, you should start at the outer edge of the footing and cover the wall up to a point 6″ above the grade around the foundation.

The first coat of mortar should be scarified (scratched) before it gets hard. A tool is made for this purpose, but you can improvise using a rake or board with nails exposed from it. Make sure you don't scrape off the first coat when scratching the surface. Scarifying is done to make the surface rough enough to make the second coat stick.

Allow the first coat to harden at least 24 hours. Dampen it and apply the second coat. Keep the coat damp for 24 hours. The foundation can be damproofed by coating the cement with hot or cold tar. Check with local blacktop contractors to see if they have a foundation service coating. They can coat your foundation with hot tar a lot faster than you could and save you the loss of some clothing.

Dampness may occur from condensation and not from actual leaks. A cause of condensation in basements is warm air coming in contact with a cool basement wall. A quick way to tell the difference between seepage and condensation is to securely tape a piece of aluminum foil about 1 foot square to the wall, making sure all four sides are as air tight as possible. After leaving it up for several days, remove the foil. If the inside is wet, it is seepage. If the outside is wet, it is condensation.

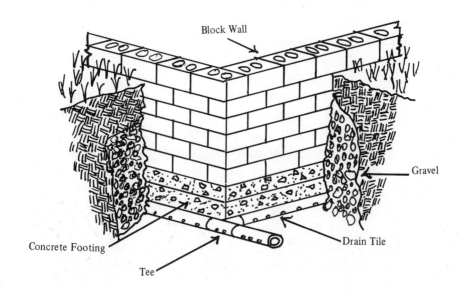

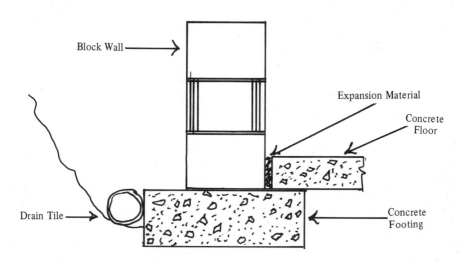

Drain tile should be placed around the perimeter of the foundation to remove any water that might run against the foundation. It is a great deterrent against water seeping in the foundation, especially if the area around the foundation doesn't drain well.

When the ground is excavated for the footing, make sure you dig enough to place a tile beside the outside edge of the footing, even with the footing. Start at the corner that is farthest away from the dry well or point where you plan to drain excess water. Slope the drain tile about a ¼" to 8 feet. Drain tiles usually have holes in them on one side. Place the tile in the excavation with the holes down. After all the tile is down, fill the area above the tile with gravel, up to about a foot from the final grade or ground level, putting in the first 12 inches or so of gravel slowly to prevent breaking the tile or disturbing the slope you created. There is a drain system on the market that is made of heavy duty plastic and comes in a roll allowing fast easy construction of the drainage system.

Interior Waterproofing

On the interior of the foundation you can use special paint made for masonry, to seal masonry surfaces and hold back the flow of water, even under pressure.

Since surface preparation is the most important step in any painting job, loose broken mortar, dirt, dust and other foreign matter, including efflorescence, spell trouble for a new coat of paint. A sound surface is important, so before painting, clean the surface well. Sealers work best when applied to an unpainted surface. Patch holes and cracks with a hydraulic cement that will fill cracks and holes, even with water leaking through the holes at the time of patching. Hydraulic cement expands when it cures and it fills holes and cracks better than other methods. Clean the area and wet it down before patching. Instructions are usually provided with the cement.

One area often overlooked when waterproofing is the crack between the floor and the wall. A crack will normally develop here during the curing of the concrete floor, as the concrete shrinks as it cures. This crack should be filled with a hydraulic cement or an epoxy mixture.

Cracks in Mortar Joints

Cracks may occur in mortar joints, perhaps resulting from the water in the mortar being absorbed by hot block surfaces or high temperatures, thus not allowing the mortar to adhere properly. Cut out the joint and use a tuck pointer or a regular jointer to fill in the joint with new mortar. If the crack is wide, or if it is through both the joints and the blocks themselves, then it occurred from external force such as setting of the wall or outside pressure. These cracks should be looked at by a professional as they might get larger or need immediate repair. If the crack is an old one and you are sure that it isn't getting bigger you can fill it with mortar or use an epoxy or latex base filler cement. There are times when a grout can be made (usually soupy mortar will work) and poured into cracks.

The completed foundation can have a decorative finish instead of just the block showing. Here is parged-on mortar with a 180° sweep made with a brush before the mortar hardened.

8

INSULATING MASONRY

Zonolite Thermo-Stud
Wall Insulation System

The Zonolite Thermo-Stud Wall Insulation System incorporates the excellent insulation properties of Zonolite Styrene Foam and a patented metal furring channel for positive mechanical attachment of the insulation foam to the interior of masonry or concrete walls. Gyp sum drywall or other interior finishing materials can be easily at tached to the metal furring channel with standard drywall screws. The Zonolite Thermo-Stud System provides an efficient wall insulation and furring system that offers substantial labor-savings when com pared to other systems.

Basic Installation

1. Remove the Thermo-Stud System from the Zonolite shipping carton. The metal furring channels are embedded in the pre-grooved Zonolite Styrene Foam Board at the factory to save time on the job site.

2. Position the 2' × 8' sheets of Thermo-Stud against the masonry wall, beginning at a corner. The styrene foam board and light gauge metal furring channel can be trimmed easily to conform to doors, win dows, elec-

164

trical outlets, etc. Job conditions may make it beneficial to install the 2′ × 8′ sheet horizontally. The pre-cut grooves allow for this field flexibility.

3. Secure the Thermo-Stud System to the substrate wall by mechanical fastening directly through the metal channel and into the substrate.

4. Position drywall over the Thermo-Stud System and fasten to the metal channel with standard drywall screws. Since the furring channels are located at 24″ centers, flexibility is offered to lay the drywall horizontally if it optimizes use of the drywall or labor.

**Complete System
Side View**

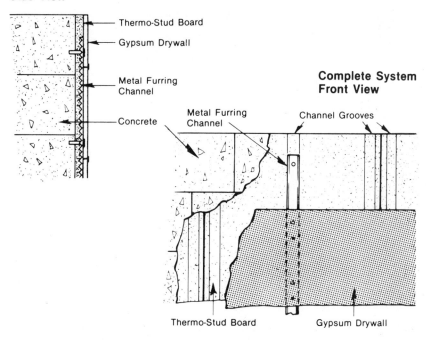

Thermo-Stud Board

Gypsum Drywall

Metal Furring
Channel

Concrete

**Complete System
Front View**

Metal Furring
Channel

Channel Grooves

Thermo-Stud Board

Gypsum Drywall

Corner Details

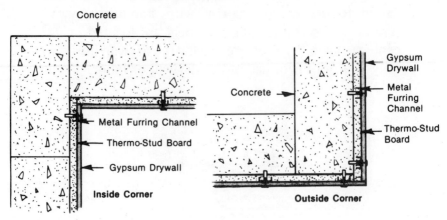

Inside Corner

- Concrete
- Metal Furring Channel
- Thermo-Stud Board
- Gypsum Drywall

Outside Corner

- Concrete
- Gypsum Drywall
- Metal Furring Channel
- Thermo-Stud Board

Typical Wall Layout
(Channel in Board Center)
Top View

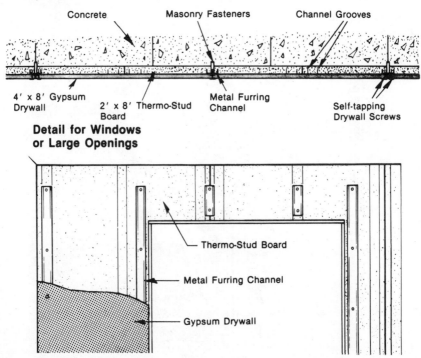

- Concrete
- Masonry Fasteners
- Channel Grooves
- 4' x 8' Gypsum Drywall
- 2' x 8' Thermo-Stud Board
- Metal Furring Channel
- Self-tapping Drywall Screws

Detail for Windows
or Large Openings

- Thermo-Stud Board
- Metal Furring Channel
- Gypsum Drywall

Zonolite Masonry Insulation

Zonolite Masonry Insulation is lightweight, free-flowing, inorganic, granular vermiculite treated for water repellency. When poured into cores and cavities of masonry walls, it forms a permanent non-setting barrier against the transmission of heat, sound and moisture. Installed during block wall construction, Zonolite Masonry Insulation is the most foolproof and economical means to insulate the wall...before the insulation opportunity is lost forever.

Basic Installation

Zonolite Masonry Insulation is recognized by owners, architects, builders and specifiers as a quick,easy and economical way of insulating masonry walls. Since it pours freely, wall heights of up to 20 feet can be readily filled in a single pour directly from the bag. No tamping or rodding is required, and there's nothing to cut, fit, patch, foam or inject. Zonolite Masonry Insulation is non-irritating and non-abrasive. Because of its ease of

installation, insulation labor costs are substantially reduced.

Benefits

Helps Reduce Heating and Cooling Costs

Zonolite Masonry Insulation helps to reduce heat transmission through walls. These heat transmission reductions are illustrated in the tables of "U" values on the following pages.

Complies With ASHRAE Standard 90-75

More and more building codes are adopting mandatory energy standards to help control energy waste. ASHRAE Standard 90-75, "Energy Conservation in New Building Design", is presently the most prominent of these standards. Using Zonolite Masonry Insulation

Approximate Coverage
4-cubic-foot bags required to fill

Sq. ft. of Wall Area	8" Block	12" Block	1" Cavity	2" Cavity	2½" Cavity	4½" Cavity
100	7	13	2	4	5	9
500	34	63	10	20	25	45
1,000	69	125	21	42	50	95
2,000	138	250	42	84	100	189
3,000	207	375	62	124	150	279
5,000	345	625	104	208	250	468
7,000	483	875	146	292	350	657
10,000	690	1,250	208	416	500	950

in the cavities of block construction helps meet the requirements of this standard with the maximum amount of fenestration. Zonolite Masonry Insulation also helps meet Federal Housing Administration standards for multi-family housing. Contact your local Zonolite representative. He can provide specific recommendations for your geographic area.

Improves the Fire Resistance of Masonry Block Walls

Many new commercial and residential masonry buildings are being constructed to meet a 4-hour fire rated wall requirement. Lightweight 8″ concrete blocks provide a 4-hour fire rated wall when filled with Zonolite Masonry Insulation. This extra "fire wall" protection provides a safety factor that allows occupants more time to escape and lessens the risk to fire fighters.

Prevents Water Permeation

A wall insulated with Zonolite Masonry Insulation virtually eliminates water permeation according to tests established by the National Bureau of Standards.

Eliminates Vapor Barrier

Zonolite Masonry Insulation eliminates the need for a vapor barrier when the average interior relative humidity does not exceed 50%. FHA bulletin UM-30 confirms this fact.

Reduces Sound Transmission

Zonolite Masonry Insulation effectively reduces the room-to-room transmission of noise by as much as 31%.

Meets the Highest Standards

Zonolite Masonry Insulation meets or exceeds the following standards:

- ■ American Society for Testing and Materials, Specification for Vermiculite Loose Fill Insulation ASTM C516-75, Type 3 and 4.
- ■ Federal Specification for Insulation, Thermal (Vermiculite), HH-I-585C.
- ■ Structural Clay Products Institute criteria for vermiculite insulated cavity walls.
- ■ National Concrete Masonry Association criteria for insulating concrete masonry units.

Zonolite® Masonry Insulation

Thermal Design "U" Factor Tables

Coefficients of Heat Transmission
Expressed in BTU/Hr./Sq.Ft./Deg. F.

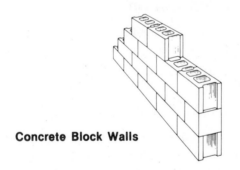

Concrete Block Walls

Wall Thickness	Type of Block	Block Only	
		Uninsulated	Insulated
6″	Lightweight	.40	.26
8″	Lightweight	.33	.17
	Heavyweight	.53	.36
12″	Lightweight	.33	.12
	Heavyweight	.46	.25

All wall designs have no interior finish.

Solid Brick and Block Walls*

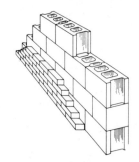

Interior Wythe		Exterior Wythe	
		4" Face Brick	4" Common Brick
6" Concrete Block (Lightweight)	Uninsulated Insulated	.34 .23	.33 .21
8" Concrete Block (Lightweight)	Uninsulated Insulated	.29 .16	.26 .15
8" Concrete Block (Heavyweight)	Uninsulated Insulated	.43 .31	.37 .28

All wall designs have no interior finish.
*No Cavity

Cavity Walls

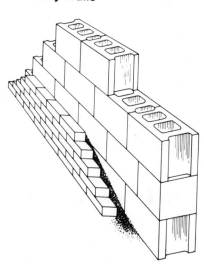

Interior Wythe		4" Exterior Wythe					
		Face Brick		Common Brick		Concrete Block (Lightweight)	
Actual Cavity Dimension ⟶		2½"	4½"	2½"	4½"	2½"	4½"
4" Concrete Block (Heavyweight)	Uninsulated	.34	.34	.30	.30	.31	.31
	Insulated	.13	.08	.13	.08	.13	.08
4" Concrete Block (Cinder) or 4" Clay Tile	Uninsulated	.30	.30	.27	.27	.25	.25
	Insulated	.13	.08	.12	.08	.12	.08
4" Concrete Block (Lightweight)	Uninsulated	.27	.27	.24	.24	.21	.21
	Insulated	.12	.08	.12	.08	.11	.07
6" Concrete Block (Lightweight)	Uninsulated	.26	.26	.23	.23	.20	.20
	Cavity Insulated	.12	.08	.11	.08	.10	.07
	Block & Cavity Insulated	.10	.07	.10	.07	.09	.07
8" Concrete Block (Lightweight)	Uninsulated	.22	.22	.21	.21	.18	.18
	Cavity Insulated	.11	.07	.11	.07	.10	.07
	Block & Cavity Insulated	.08	.06	.08	.06	.08	.06
4" Face Brick	Uninsulated	.37	.37	.33	.33	.27	.27
	Insulated	.14	.09	.13	.08	.12	.08
4" Common Brick	Uninsulated	.33	.33	.29	.29	.24	.24
	Insulated	.13	.08	.13	.08	.12	.08

All wall designs have no interior finish.

Zonolite Styrene Foam

Zonolite Styrene Foam is an expanded polystyrene which meets a wide variety of insulation requirements at a low installed cost. A high quality, molded plastic material, Zonolite Styrene Foam can be used to insulate building foundations, walls and roofs. Zonolite Styrene Foam is a uniformly high quality product, backed by a nationwide network of sales representatives, technical services, and distributors.

8″ Lightweight Block with ½″ Interior Gypsum Drywall

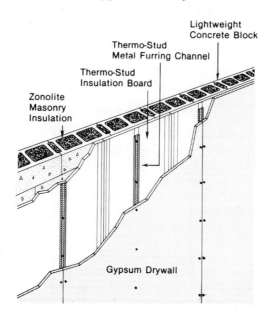

Lightweight
Concrete Block

Thermo-Stud
Metal Furring Channel

Thermo-Stud
Insulation Board

Zonolite
Masonry
Insulation

Gypsum Drywall

6″ Precast Concrete with ½″ Interior Gypsum Drywall

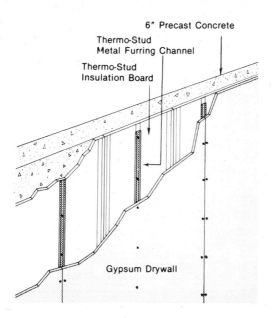

6″ Precast Concrete

Thermo-Stud
Metal Furring Channel

Thermo-Stud
Insulation Board

Gypsum Drywall

8" Lightweight Block; 4" Exterior Wythe Face Brick; (1" Cavity); with ½" Interior Gypsum Drywall

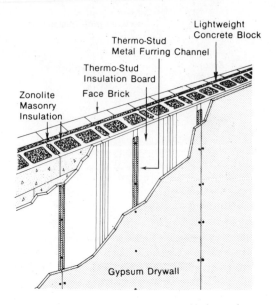

Lightweight Concrete Block

Thermo-Stud Metal Furring Channel

Thermo-Stud Insulation Board

Zonolite Masonry Insulation

Face Brick

Gypsum Drywall

Benefits

High Performance Insulation
- Thermally efficient — excellent insulation at a minimum thickness
- Cost effective — substantial savings over other foam products per R-value
- Moisture resistant — no mechanical damage or loss of thermal properties
- Durable — high strength-to-weight ratio
- Chemically resistant — to most acids and alkalis
- Permanent — does not lose R-value with age
- Light weight — easy to handle and trim
- Meets code requirements

Typical Applications

Versatile Insulation

- Building perimeters
- Cavity walls
- Sheathing board
- Cold storage
- Panel construction
- Roof decks
- Flotation
- Siding backerboard
- Concrete tilt-up panels

Meets Code Requirements

Zonolite Styrene Foam meets or exceeds many flammability, insulation, or code requirements. Specifically, Zonolite Styrene Foam can be manufactured to comply with the following military and federal specifications*:

Federal Spec. HHI-524-B
Military Spec. MIL-P-0019644-B
Military Spec. MIL-P-40619
Military Spec. MIL-P-43110
Army Corps of Engineers CE-204
Coast Guard CG-256
Air Force AFM 88-15

All information in this chapter was supplied by Grace Construction Products Division.

*Consult your local Zonolite Representative for specific density requirements to satisfy sub-classification of these specifications.

9

GLASS BLOCKS

To many people, glass blocks have been just a way of letting in light and providing privacy. But today, there is a wide selection of styles and sizes from which to choose, and more people are beginning to see that glass blocks have many advantages over other kinds of construction materials.

Aside from providing privacy, glass blocks are sound deadeners. When they are made, they are fused together creating a vacuum inside the block, giving the glass block an insulating value as good as a 12″ masonry wall. Once they are installed, they require little maintainence.

You can ask your local building supply dealer to show you the many sizes and styles available in your area. You can choose glass blocks that filter light or admit direct light, interior plain blocks and some beautiful decorative glass blocks that combine ceramic coatings with clear glass for a dramatic effect. Glass block panels, regardless of area or size, are non-loadbearing and require a space at the top to take care of expansion or deflection of the lintel over the opening. They are made in the following sizes: 3″ × 6″, 4″ × 8″, 6″ × 6″, 6″ × 8″, 8″ × 8″, 4″ × 12″, and 12″ × 12″. Using different size blocks together will sometimes solve a problem with the size of the opening. You can use a 3″ × 6″, a 4″ × 8″ and a 6″ × 8″ with a 6″ and 8″ square block. You can use a 4″ × 12″ and a 12″ × 12″ together.

Check the Opening

Before starting, check the opening to see if you have an adequate opening for glass blocks. They are next to impossible for the homeowner to cut with ordinary tools, so before tearing out a wood window, measure the rough opening to see if the blocks you plan to use will fit.

To check the opening size, add the size of the block plus ⅜″ joint, both in length and height. If you are putting the glass blocks in a wood opening you might be able to make up some of the extra space with thin pieces of wood. Use wood moldings around the finished wall to cover the edges and always make sure the sill or bottom of the opening is level, to help get better results. If you are going to build in a wood frame, make sure the sides are plumb (straight up and down) before you start.

If you want to build a glass block wall of 25 square feet or less with a maximum of 5 feet in width, and a maximum height of 7 feet, this panel can be mortared in solidly at the jamb (sides). It is necessary to keep a finger space (¾″) between the brick and the block panel so the mortar can "key in" at the jamb and secure the panel.

Tools Required

Along with the tools required to remove the wood frame, you will need a trowel, a level, and a jointer.

Begin by marking the sides of the jamb with a pencil, at the heights you will lay the glass blocks. Include the thickness of the joint, either ¼″ or ⅜″. Doing this will help you get the same size joint and keep the blocks level.

For small projects, you can buy a bag of mortar cement that is premixed, and just add water to it. Try to deep the mix stiff but workable as this will make it easier to lay the blocks. Since the blocks don't soak up moisture from the mortar, wet mortar will allow the blocks to slide around.

Installing Glass Blocks

When you are installing glass blocks over an exterior wall, you should first cover the sill area with asphalt roof cement. Mark the area with lines so you won't get too much on the sill. Make the coating ¼" thick. Now use expansion strips (these can be bought with the blocks) in the top and sides, held in place with a light coating of roof cement. Once the cement has dried on the sill, spread a layer of mortar cement on the asphalt for the first course. Set the first course of block in the cement, adjusting the height to the marks you made on the side to gauge your height. Put mortar on the end of each block before you lay it in the bed joint. It is much easier and makes a fuller end joint.

Reinforcing Glass Blocks

After the first course is laid, you may want to reinforce the wall with a special reinforcing wire that is made to lay in the wall in the horizontal joints. When you have laid all the blocks in the panel, joint them with a jointing tool, to compress the mortar and make the finished wall stronger and better looking. At the ends and at spaces requiring caulking, gently rake out some of the mortar, and then caulk the joint. As the mortar dries, clean off the face of the wall (and back also) with a cloth or smooth bristled brush. Stop cleaning if you are digging out the joints and wait until it sets longer. If you prefer, you can use white mortar for lighter color joints. You can use ⅜" joints instead of ¼" to make up a little space if needed, but joints should not be larger than ⅜" as doing this will weaken the wall. If you are installing glass blocks in a masonry wall you can cement them directly to the existing wall. In either masonry or wooden walls always remember that you have to leave at least ½" at the top for expansion.

Glass Block Details

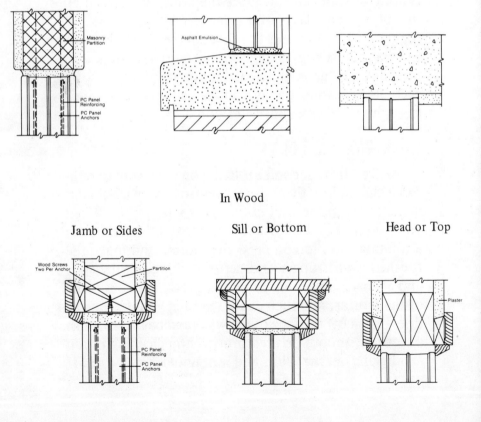

In Masonry

Jamb or Sides   Sill or Bottom   Head or Top

In Wood

Jamb or Sides   Sill or Bottom   Head or Top

Materials for 100 sq. ft. of the following:

	size block		
	6" block	8" block	12" block
Amount of block	400	200	100
Mortar (cubic ft,)	4.3	3.2	2.2

Old windows are constructed with wood, steel, or aluminum frames. Wood and aluminum frames are very easily removed using a claw hammer or a crowbar. Steel frames may require cutting with a hacksaw. Whatever the case, remove the old frames entirely.

Before actually mortaring the glass block in place, make a test run. Place loose block in each window opening to create one complete horizontal and vertical row. Place folded cardboard or wood spacers between the glass blocks to simulate even mortar joints. Once you have the complete horizontal and vertical row in place, put check marks on the wall surrounding the window opening to line up with the top and bottom of each spacer.

When installing glass block in a masonry opening, you should first put a layer of mortar on the windowsill and smooth it out with a trowel to create an even bed of mortar. Then, put a layer of mortar on the side of the opening where the first block will butt against the wall. Put mortar on one vertical edge of each block and place in position to create the first course. Repeat this until all blocks are in place.

Let the glass blocks "settle" for approximately two hours or until the mortar is almost dry. Then smooth all the joints to remove excess mortar for a clean, professional-looking job. The smoothing procedure will compact the mortar to create a moistureproof seal.

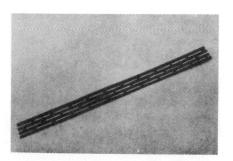

PC Panel Anchors—To be used for supporting panels up to 100 sq. ft. in area where permitted by building code requirements. Spaced and installed in accordance with PC specifications. Panel Anchors are No. 20 gage perforated steel galvanized after fabrication. Available in 2'0" lengths, 1¾" wide.

PC Expansion Strips—To be used in expansion spaces at jambs and heads installed in accordance with PC specifications. Available in the following size: ⁷⁄₁₆" x 4⅛" x 24" (for use in chase construction). For panel anchor construction, standard 4⅛"-wide strips can easily be cut to 3" width required.

PC Panel Reinforcing—To be used in horizontal joints of glass block panels, spaced and installed in accordance with PC specification. Panel Reinforcing is formed of two No. 9 gage galvanized wires spread 2" apart with No. 14 gage galvanized cross wires welded every 8". Available in 8' lengths. Also available with a spread of 1⅝" in 10' lengths, with cross wires every 10".

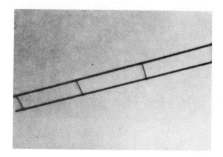

10

FIREPLACES

Throughout history, brick has been used to build fireplaces because it is noncombustible and because it collects heat and reflects it into the room. But scientific innovations in fireplace design have been critical to the development of the modern, efficient brick fireplace, and they are important to remember as you plan and build the fireplace of your dreams.

The practice of making indoor fires or creating fireplaces probably dates from the first cave fires of early man. But the science of planning and building controlled indoor fires is most often traced to early Greek and Roman civilizations. Usually set in the center of a large room, the fireplace was generally a stone or brick platform set beneath an opening in the roof to allow smoke to escape.

Wall fireplaces were not developed until sometime in the 11th century. Early wall fireplaces were created by placing the platform or hearth against the wall. An overhanging hood of brick or metal directed smoke out of the building through a channel in the wall.

As multi-level castles were built in the Gothic period, the need for fireplaces on each floor caused the development of two major fireplace innovations: the recessed opening and the chimney. Fireplaces quickly became more than heating and cooking centers; they became major design features.

The Romans used a crude form of radiant heating in the 12th century by passing flame and smoke into passages in the floor and ceilings. But, it was not until the 17th century that much attention was directed to efficient heat circulation. By creating duct openings below and beside the fireplace opening, cool air was warmed as it passed the brick in the hot chamber and was directed out vents above the fire.

Benjamin Franklin, an authority on many things including heat circulating fireplaces, is remembered as the creator of the Franklin Stove and the Pennsylvania Fireplace. But it was another Benjamin, Franklin's American born contemporary, whose innovations are responsible for much of fireplace design today.

Benjamin Thompson, dubbed Count Rumford after moving to Europe (he was born in Rumford, New Hampshire), continued to use brick while many were switching to metal. Rumford fireplaces, as they are called now, had smaller and shallower chambers than others of the 18th century and featured a narrow back with wide sides which flare outward. The smoke shelf and throat was set far forward and quite high. This combination of features made the Rumford fireplace highly efficient and set the pattern for fireplace construction techniques that are still in use.

Building a good brick fireplace is much more than creating an attractive brick wall and fireproof chamber. Unless it is properly planned and constructed, a fireplace may waste energy, supply too little or too much heat, or even deliver smoke into a room. A basic knowledge of fireplace parts and their function, as well as the relationship betweeen a fireplace and the room it's in, will help you build the best possible brick fireplace.

Proper combustion of fuel and delivery of all smoke up the chimney are important and relating fac-

tors. Success in achieving these conditions depends on:
(1) the shape and dimensions of the fire chamber; (2)
the proper location of the fireplace throat and its relationship to the smoke shelf; and (3) the ratio of the flue
area to the fireplace opening. The table a few pages
ahead shows typical sizes of singlefaced fireplace openings and their relationship to corresponding flue sizes.

Consider Sizes Carefully

Radiation of the most heat into the room is directly related to the shape and dimensions of the combustion chamber. So careful consideration must be given
to the size of a fireplace best suited for the room in
which it will be located. If it is too small, it may function properly but not produce enough heat. Converse-
ly, a fire in an oversized fireplace might be too hot for
the room, requiring a larger chimney which would
draw excess air through doors and windows--a great
waste of fuel.

A 12′ × 25′ living room (300 sq. ft.) is well served by
a fireplace with a 30″ × 36″ opening. For larger rooms,
the width may be increased. The fireplace opening
should not be too high, rarely more than 32 inches
above the hearth for most standard width openings.
The first two columns in the fireplace dimensions table
ahead give the correct widths and heights of proper
fireplace openings. All dimensions may be varied
slightly to meet regular brick courses and joints.

The Correct Shape Is Important

The shape of the firebox or combustion chamber
has a direct effect on the draft and the amount of heat
radiated into the room. The slope of the back of this
chamber throws the flame forward and leads the gases
with increasing velocity through the throat.

This home had a stone veneer half way up the side. The fireplace was to be constructed here, centered on the living room wall. A hole was drilled through the wall to show the center of the new fireplace and the dimensions were marked off. A rented power saw that takes a large masonry blade was used to cut through the stone. Loose stone that fell out of the sides was replaced later.

The masonry saw. This is a large saw that can be rented or bought. Also available in smaller models. The expensive blade is industrial diamond. When using a masonry saw, be extremely careful, for it can cut practically anything, including fingers.

The firebox should be laid with firebrick bonded by thin joints of fireclay mortar. The back and end walls should be at least eight inches thick to support the weight of the chimney. Ease of construction and fire safety depend on the size and shape of the brick and their ability to withstand high temperatures without warping, cracking or deteriorating.

Constructing the Fireplace

Very few fireplaces are exactly alike, but the interiors of almost all fireplaces of the front opening type are the same. We see in this chapter the construction of a fireplace in a home where the wall had to be cut in order to install the fireplace. It is a lot cheaper to construct a fireplace in a new home as the home is being built. The materials are dirty and take up a lot of room and in an existing home the construction of a new fireplace can be a nuisance to a housewife because of the dust and dirt. The end result can justify the inconvenience, though, if you have patience.

Digging the Foundation

The foundation that supports the fireplace should extend below the frost line in your area. Check with local contractors or building supply dealers to find out what this depth is.

The footing should consist of reinforced concrete and solid masonry to support the weight. The dimensions should be at least 8″ and 12″ thick. The footing should have reinforcing rods or bars in a grid about 12″ apart about in the middle (height) of the footing. Never support a fireplace or chimney by wooden beams, posts, or floors. They can in time crack, bend, warp or rot and release the load to cause further damage.

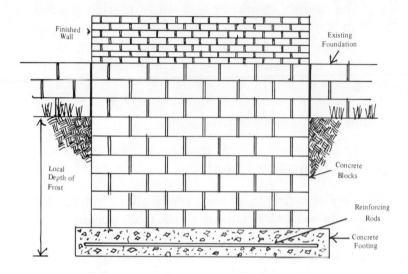

The footing for the fireplace can be poured without forms if you are careful and make the outside dimensions of the excavation at least 16 inches wider than the finished wall. Remember you will have to work in the hole laying the blocks so you will have to allow room to stand beside the wall as you erect it.

The footing should be allowed to cure for a day before you begin to lay the block foundation on it.

The block foundation can be extended to the grade line or to the top of the existing foundation, depending on personal taste. It is sometimes hard to match the old wall so starting your exterior finish at ground level sometimes looks better.

The fireplace pictured in this chapter was built in cold weather. This requires a covering which is sufficient to keep a lot of heat from escaping from the house when you aren't working on the wall. Use heavy polyethylene or canvas when not working on the project.

Opening the Wall

The wall you are about to open might be a load bearing wall and therefore should be braced. Look in the basement or celler or in the crawl space under the floor of the room where the fireplace will be built. You will be able to see which way the joists run across the room. The ceiling joists should run the same way especially in new homes. Once this is known you can put a brace made out of 2″ × 4″, 2″ × 6″ or 2″ × 8″ lumber depending on the amount of weight above the opening (1 floor, 2 floor, etc.).

The fireplace may extend into the room depending on design, and when it does you will also have to cut an

Footings for fireplaces can be poured when pouring the footing for the foundation. The footing should be at least 12″ thick and reinforced.

opening in the floor. (Finish the wall opening before cutting the floor.)

You will see that only three studs have to be removed. The opening was cut out in sections as it kept heat loss down.

If the joists run the opposite way, then place the braces directly above or below the joists.

Opening the Floor

Before cutting the floor open--actually, before cutting any opening--you should make double checks of your measurements since it will be next to impossible to replace the extra ¼″ or so you might have cut off accidentally.

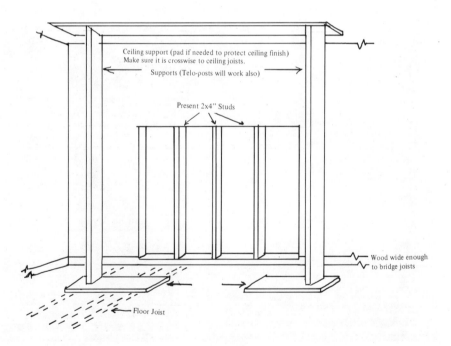

Ceiling support (pad if needed to protect ceiling finish) Make sure it is crosswise to ceiling joists.

Supports (Telo-posts will work also)

Present 2x4″ Studs

Wood wide enough to bridge joists

Floor Joist

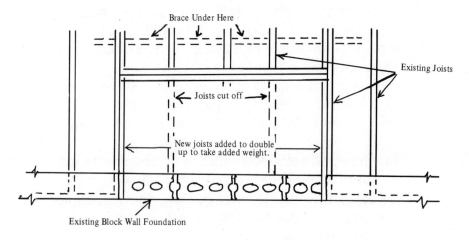

Top view

When the floor joists run at right angles to the face of the fireplace.

If the joists happen to run parallel with the face of the fireplace you can brace the joists to be cut and make new braces as shown in the next illustration.

(The dimensions vary with the design and width of the extended hearth)

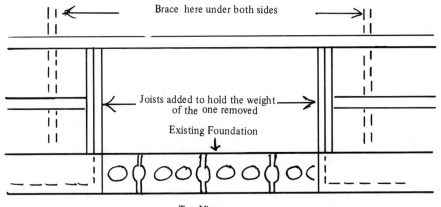

Top View

Check to see the way the floor joists are running. If they are running parallel with the wall you are working on, you will have a little easier job then if they run at right angles to the fireplaces.

First put bracing beneath any joist that will be cut. In a crawl space it could be a pier and some wood cut to fit for a permanent brace. When the basement is to be used and the bracing will be torn down then you can use either telo-posts or wood with top and bottom braces.

The concrete subhearth should be allowed to cure for a day before work continues. Cover the opening securely to prevent drafts into the house, and keep rain or snow off the surface.

When a block base isn't brought up inside the foundation for an extra flue or just for support then the opening can be filled with reinforced concrete. Nail a strip of wood 2″ × 4″ or 1″ × 2″ around the perimeter as shown in the illustration. Cut a piece of ¾″ plywood to fit as tight as possible so there will be no leakage of concrete around it. Nail the plywood to this strip around the hole. Put a brace under the center of the concrete (plywood) form to support it while it is setting up.

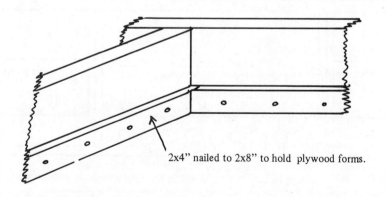

2x4" nailed to 2x8" to hold plywood forms.

Side View

Reinforcement Is a Must

When building a subhearth such as this, you must reinforce the concrete sufficently to support the weight of the extended hearth. A block base is recommended if the hearth projects more than 16″-18″ past the foundation wall (inside).

The bricks are run above the floor level, and the opening is braced to hold the weight of the concrete. Reinforcing rods are placed in the concrete. The concrete is finished off just below the floor at least 6″ thick. (104)

The inside of the base of the fireplace can be filled in with any kind of masonry. Here, we see cinder brick used for economy. All parts of the fireplace should have some mortar bonding it together.

Plastic or canvas keeps the house warm when work is halted.

Bricks are laid up outside about 48″ above the finished floor. If the hearth is even with the floor, you can lay the brick around the edge of the firebox opening. If not, leave wall ties from the last bricks laid inside to join the rest with a stronger bond.

The concrete subhearth should be allowed to cure for a day before work continues. Cover the opening securely to prevent drafts into the house, and keep rain or snow off the surface.

The Hearth

The hearth should always be laid with firebrick, bonded together by fireclay. The joints should be thin, and the firebrick laid flat. The first course of firebrick may be laid in a bed joint of regular mortar, the side and end joints should be of fireclay.

Firebrick is expensive, so planning ahead is important. Lay out the base (hearth) without mortar, checking your spacing as you do it. You can mark in pencil the outline of the firebox on the top of these dry bricks since you might want to move them over one way or the other for looks.

You can pick up the bricks one or two at a time and lay your pattern out more easily.

Here is how the firebrick was laid out for this hearth. This fireplace has a raised, extended hearth so block was laid on the subhearth first, to raise the level of the hearth.

Use firebrick to cover only the area needed for the firebox. The rest of the area can be filled with concrete block or brick bats. Once you have established the hearth and laid one course from the sides and the back you can spread a light layer of sand over the hearth to keep mortar and fireclay from sticking as it drops or splashes on the hearth.

The Firebox

Check to see if your measurements for the angle, length and width are correct. Lay the firebrick in tight joints but keep them level around the box. If you lay one course around at a time, you can make leveling it a lot easier.

Laying the firebox. Firebrick can be cut with a sharp brick set or chisel, or they can be sawed with a masonry blade.

If you lay the firebrick flat they will provide a stronger wall and retain the heat in the box better. Cut the corners so they run over each other in alternate courses. Put firebrick chips and fireclay in any large voids so there won't be any leaks.

The Firebox-Back Wall

After you have laid up the back wall approximately 14" you should begin to splay (slant) the back in toward the front. The angle of the splay depends on the size of the fireplace. The side bricks are cut to allow the angle of the splay. An easy way to get the firebrick to angle in toward the front is to lay a thicker bed joint in the rear of the top of the last course. It is also a little

The completed firebox. Always check to see if you are constructing the right size firebox for the damper you have bought. Most dampers come with instructions.

easier if you can buy split firebrick. They are only half as thick and can be used to return the splay back to level for placement of the damper.

A lintel--angle iron--must be installed above the opening of the fireplace to support the weight of the masonry above. Lintels are usually $3\frac{1}{2}'' \times 3'' \times \frac{1}{4}$ thick, but a larger one would be required if the load were to be very heavy, or the opening wider than 48''. The lintel should rest on each side of the opening by at least 4''. When you install the lintel, leave a small space at each end for expansion, as metal expands when it is heated. A common practice is to wrap the ends of the lintels with insulation. Check to see that the lintel is level.

It is a general practice to construct the walls of a fireplace at least 8'' thick. Some building codes might want them thicker, but they should never be thinner. Any trim made out of a combustible material should be at least 8'' from the opening and the masonry of the fire-place and chimney should have a clearence of $1\frac{1}{2}''$ to 2'' from combustibles.

When designing the fireplace to provide a pleasing appearance, make the jambs or sides proportionate to the height. The side should be at least 16'' wide and, if the fireplace is in a large room, the jambs can be wider for appearance. If a mantle is desired over the opening it should be at least 12'' above the fireplace opening.

An ash dump can be built into the hearth to allow ashes to be dumped into a hollow pit in the foundation, for later removal through a cleanout door. The size of the ash pit is up to individual taste. The ash dump door takes the place of one firebrick in the hearth and should be placed toward the rear in the center. If you plan on having an ash dump, plan ahead when you pour the concrete for the subhearth by making a small form slightly larger than a firebrick. Place the form on the

BRICK FIREPLACE DIMENSIONS

Finished Fireplace Opening				Flue Sizes	
A	B	C			
Width	Height	Depth		Modular	Standard
24	24	16		8 X 12	8½ X 8½
26	24	16		8 X 12	8½ X 8½
28	24	16		8 X 12	8½ X 13
30	29	16		12 X 12	8½ X 13
32	29	16		12 X 12	8½ X 13
36	29	16		12 X 12	13 X 13
40	29	16		12 X 16	13 X 13
42	32	16		16 X 16	13 X 13
48	32	18		16 X 16	13 X 13

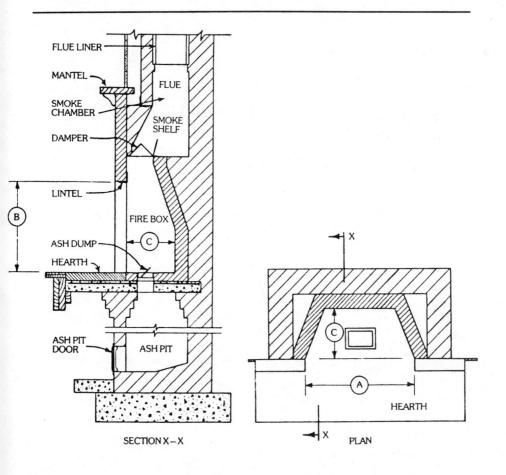

SECTION X–X   PLAN

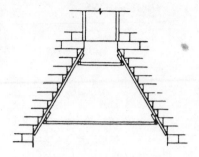

Smoke chamber

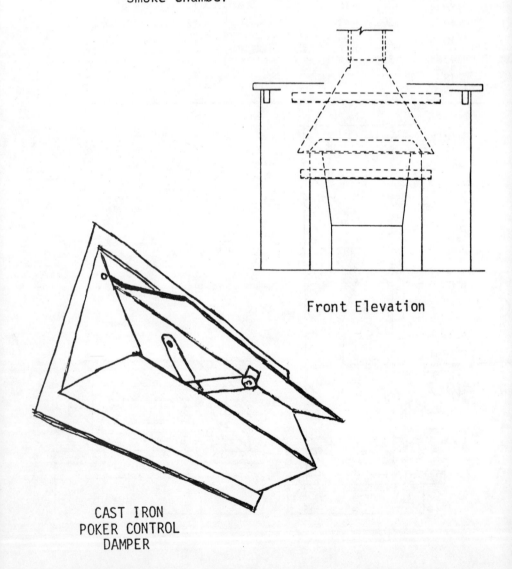

Front Elevation

CAST IRON
POKER CONTROL
DAMPER

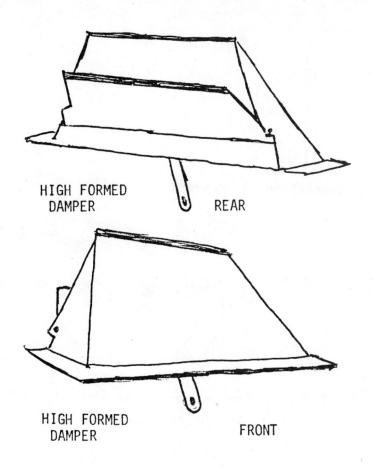

HIGH FORMED
DAMPER   REAR

HIGH FORMED
DAMPER   FRONT

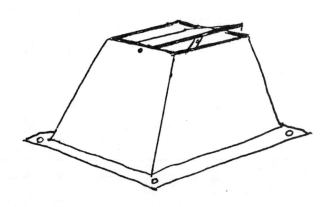

UNIVERSAL DAMPER
FOR
OPEN-SIDED FIREPLACES

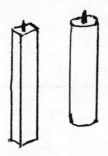

2" Square and 2" round Posts

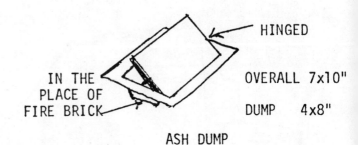

IN THE PLACE OF FIRE BRICK

HINGED

OVERALL 7x10"

DUMP   4x8"

ASH DUMP

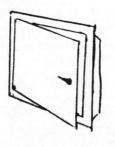

OVERALL 10x10"

DOOR 8-1/2x8-1/2"

CLEANOUT DOOR

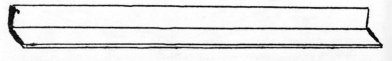

ANGLE IRON LINTEL

3-1/2x3-1/2"
1/4" THICK

¾″ plywood where you plan to have the cleanout box and tack it to the plywood. The hole can later be drilled out.

When you have run the brick facing up about 28″ for a 36″ opening, place the lintel on the bricks and lay the next course across the lintel. There should be at least 12″ of brick work above the top of the opening.

Taking great pains when laying the face of the fireplace to make sure it is level, plumb and the bricks square, even and joints the same size, will make the final appearence much better.

The face of the fireplace almost finished. Note how the opening in the wall isn't any bigger than it has to be. You can leave the sheetrock above and apply cement to it since it is fire resistant.

The firebox was built first, then the face was run up past the firebox opening using a lintel for support. Now the damper can be installed on the firebrick, about 6" above the lintel. Set it tight against the brickwork to prevent smoke leaks. Use fire clay around the edges and fill any voids.

The Damper

The damper is usually a cast iron frame made with a hinged lid which can be opened to different degrees to control the fire. The damper regulates the draft and can be shut off when the fireplace isn't being used to save heat from the main heating system from escaping up the chimney. There are many companies making dampers. Some make dampers that incorporate lintels in the form of the damper to save work. At least one company makes a damper that also forms part of the smoke chamber. Other types of dampers are made for two and three open sided fireplaces. You can see these in the illustrations.

The Throat

Proper construction of the throat is very important for a fireplace to work properly. The sides of the fireplace should be made vertical up to the throat and the throat should be made to start from 6″ to 8″ above the bottom edge of the lintel. The area of the throat should not be less than the area of the flue. The length should be equal to the width of the fireplace opening. The width of the throat will depend on the width of the metal damper opening. About 5″ above the throat you should start sloping in (corbelling) toward the area where the flue will start.

The Smoke Shelf

The smoke shelf is built behind the damper to prevent downdrafts. It is made by setting the brickwork at the top of the throat back to the line of the flue wall for the length of the throat. The depth of the smoke shelf might be 6″ to 16″ depending on the thickness of the fireplace, but it should be concave to make air circulate better. The smoke chamber is the area from the throat to the flue. The side walls of the smoke chamber should slope from the smoke shelf up to the flue opening at a 30°angle and the sides should be as smooth as possible to promote draft, and lessen the accumulation of soot.

Brick work around the chimney flues and the fireplace should be laid with cement mortar since it is more resistant to the action of heat and flue gases than lime mortar. A good mortar for use in setting flue linings and chimney masonry, except firebrick, consists of 1 part Portland cement, 1 part hydrated lime and 6 parts clean sand measured by volume. (Firebrick should be laid with fireclay.)

The Beginning of the Flue

The flue should begin at the top of the smoke chamber, and it should be the right proportion to be effective. Engineers have worked out exact proportions of the size of the flue to the size of the opening in the front of the fireplace, and in relation to the height of the chimney.

Chimneys have been built without flue liners, but these chimneys are not as safe as those with flue liners or as efficient. In those without flue liners, the mortar and bricks disintegrate in time, due to flue gases and heat. These type of chimneys are dangerous fire hazards. Any crack at all will allow smoke and possibly flame into a building.

The top of the smoke dome. You can see how the firebrick was corbelled in on the sides and from the front toward the back. The back wall of the smoke dome was brought straight up from the smoke shelf. The area around the smoke dome should be filled in solidly with masonry.

Flue Linings

Flue linings are made of vitrified fireclay, and are able to withstand rapid fluctuations in temperature and the action of flue gases. They are made for use in masonry construction.

An 8″ × 8″ flue liner will fit into a 16″ × 20″ chimney block. Larger flues are made in 12″ × 12″, 12″ × 16″, and 16″ × 16″ sizes although there aren't chimney blocks made for these sizes. (The weight of these size chimney blocks make them awkward, therefore unprofitable to make or use.) Round flue liners are also made and they are more efficient because of their smoothness. But square or rectangular ones are easier to use in brick and block construction.

The proper way to build with flue liners is to lay them in a full bed of fireclay or mortar mixed with fireclay (this is important because of breakage). Flue liners should be built as straight up and down (plumb) as possible. If you must tilt the tile to get around a projection, the angle should never be more than 30°. A sharp angle will effect the draft.

Every chimney should be given a smoke test before it is used for a full fire. Build a small paper fire at the bottom of the flue or on the hearth. Put some tar paper on the fire to create a lot of dark smoke (make sure the damper is open before you light the fire). Once you have the smoke going up the chimney, cover the top for a few minutes (use something that won't burn and or burn you). After a few minutes any smoke leaks should show up and now would be the easiest time to fix them.

Chimneys should be constructed at least three feet above flat roofs and two feet above the peak of pitched roofs. A large building or tree too close to the chimney can cause poor draft.

Chimney Caps

To remedy poor draft you can construct a chimney cap on the top of the chimney. This cap or hood can be made of metal, stone or concrete. (Some building supply dealers have precast concrete caps. Caps made of masonry should be put about 8"-12" above the finished chimney. Make sure the flue is only about 4" above the finished chimney. You may have to lay one more block to give yourself enough clearance above the flue. If the flue sticks up about 4" then you can lay three bricks in mortar flat at each corner and place a cap (in mortar) on these. Measure the outside before you buy the material to make sure the cap is large enough to cover the top.

The finished fireplace. The bricks were laid on the sides in what is called stack bond. Over the opening they were laid in soldier course. The mason used all dark-colored brick for effect. The extended hearth is made of black slate. A carpenter who excels in making furniture was called in to make an enclosure of solid hand-rubbed cherry.

The chimney on this fireplace has been corbelled out two courses and then back into its original size. This is purely decorative.

Fancy Tops

The top of a chimney doesn't have to conform to a given shape and therefore can be made with some design to add a little flair. Some old Victorian homes have fancy tops on the fireplace chimneys, often the mark of the mason who built the chimney and of the architecture itself.

The outside of the finished fireplace.

Modified Fireplaces

Modified fireplaces are manufactured fireplace units, made of heavy metal, designed to be set in place and concealed by the usual brick work or other construction. They contain all the essential fireplace parts (firebox, damper, throat, smoke shelf, and chamber). The only parts that are not part of the whole unit are the grills for air passages.

Modified fireplaces offer two advantages: 1. The correctly designed and proportioned firebox provides a ready made form for the masonry, which reduces the

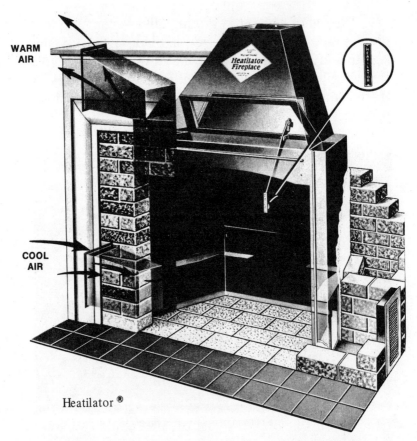

Heatilator ®

A modified fireplace. It has its advantages over the standard fireplaces.

chance of faulty construction and assures a smoke free fireplace. 2. When properly installed, the better designed units heat more efficiently than ordinary fireplaces. They circulate heat into cold corners of rooms and can deliver heated air through ducts to upper or adjoining rooms.

The use of modified fireplaces is not a perfect guarantee of a trouble free fireplace, because the chimney still has to be carefully and properly constructed.

Smokey Fireplaces

Smokey fireplaces have different causes. To determine the cause, take a piece of wood about 6″ wide and longer than the fireplace opening. Start a fire and wait for it to start to smoke into the room. Hold the piece of wood flat against the top of the opening. Now lower it until no smoke comes into the room. Mark the sides of the opening with a pencil on the bottom edge of the board. Remove the board before it begins to overheat and burn. You can now build a panel of some **noncombustible material** and secure it at this level across the top of the opening. Another way is to raise the bottom the same distance that has been marked off (instead of lowering the top) for the top, by adding a layer of firebrick. You might be able to purchase split firebrick (1½ thickness). Sometimes smokey fireplaces will need the flue raised a foot or two, or a cap put on top. Having a cement wash put around the flue (sloped cement) helps as it promotes draft and keeps water out.

Important Points to Remember

Never build a fireplace directly across the room from an outside door. A gust of wind could cause the fireplace to throw smoke and sparks into the room. In a home with forced air heat, the fireplace shouldn't have a register near the front because a downdraft might be created bringing smoke from the fireplace into the room.

In newer homes, and some better built older one's, the fireplace might not work properly for no apparent reason. It could be due to lack of an oxygen supply for the combustion of the fire. You might have to leave a door or window ajar slightly to provide enough oxygen for combustion. If the fireplace doesn't have enough oxygen it will draw air down the chimney and cause a smokey situation in the room.

Keep in mind that a fireplace isn't a simple weekend job. it will require cutting out the side of your home (for an outside chimney), opening the floor in front of the fireplace, and when the fireplace is finished, rebuilding the wood trim around the fireplace. If you can, ask a local mason for some advice on your particular project.

11

CHIMNEYS

All fuel burning stoves and fireplaces need some type of chimney. Interior chimneys are sometimes better because they stay warmer longer than exterior chimneys. For this reason, they draw better. A chimney should be designed to provide sufficient draft to get rid of the smoke and hot gases coming from the heating system or the fireplace. Construction is easy if you follow some rules for proper size, height, etc.

Make Adequate Footings

Chimneys are very heavy, weighing up to 150 pounds per cubic foot. For this reason you should make sure that you have constructed an adequate footing. Use concrete for the footing. Footings are designed to spread the load of the chimney over a wide area (about 8″ past the edges of the chimney) with a minimum thickness of 8″. Fireplace chimneys should have thicker footings because of their additional weight. A footing of 12″ thick will support most fireplaces.

If you are working inside the exterior of the foundation, you will still have to provide a new footing because the floor of most basements is usually only 4″ thick. Always check the local building codes to see if a chimney has to conform to a code. The code might give you the correct depth required below the frost line. If not, check with local contractors to see what the standard is.

Flue Linings

Flue linings should always be used in new chimney construction, since they lessen the chance of fire and provide a better draft. Flue linings in chimneys should be laid in fireclay or Portland cement mortar because they are more resistant to heat than regular mortar.

The joints should be full and smooth to prevent leaks and places where soot can collect. If it isn't possible to build the chimney perfectly plumb because of a projection in the house, then you can cut the flue tile to get around the projection, as shown in the illustration, but never more than 30° out of plumb. The brick around the bend can be corbelled as shown. If you were building with chimney block, you would not be able to corbell as easily. It would take a longer space since the blocks are 8″ thick. With blocks, it might be easier to cut the projection off instead.

Changing the Size of Chimneys

In some situations, you might have a small interior chimney that would look better if it were a brick wider. Just below the roof (16″) start to corbell the brick out 1″ each course. In just four courses you will have corbelled the chimney out one extra brick. (See the illustration.)

Soot Pocket and Cleanout

A soot pocket and a cleanout door are recommended for each flue run in the chimney. If you connect two flues to the same cleanout, you will cause air from one tile to be drawn into the other tile preventing

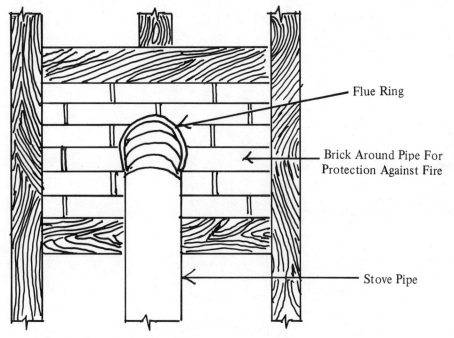

Flue Ring

Brick Around Pipe For
Protection Against Fire

Stove Pipe

Correct Installation Through a Wood Wall

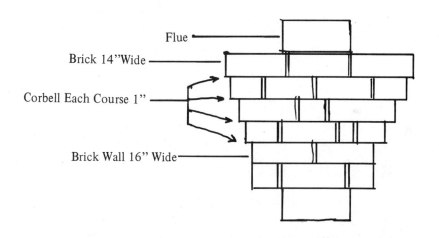

Flue

Brick 14"Wide

Corbell Each Course 1"

Brick Wall 16" Wide

Correct Way to Corbell Before Going Through Roof

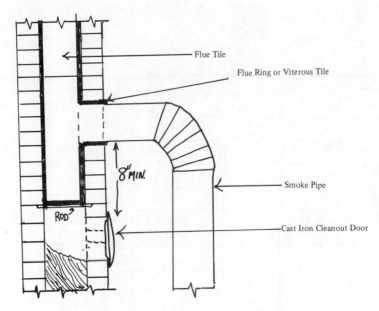

Flue Tile

Flue Ring or Viterous Tile

Smoke Pipe

Cast Iron Cleanout Door

8" MIN.

ROD

Correct Way to Construct a Cleanout Door

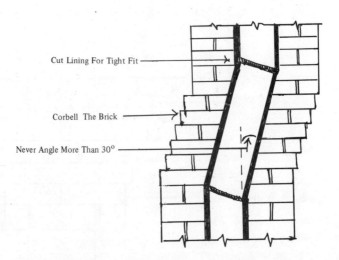

Cut Lining For Tight Fit

Corbell The Brick

Never Angle More Than 30°

Correct Way to Bend Chimney Around a Projection

good draft. A soot pocket should be deep enough to allow you to put a cleanout door above it.

Cleanout doors are made out of cast iron or steel and should be cemented in firmly. The best way to cut a chimney block for the cleanout door is to cut it with an electric saw and a masonry cut off blade. Mark the outline of the cleanout door on the block and cut as much as you can with the saw, finish it off with a hammer and a chisel. (Wear goggles and observe safety precautions: cement jumps easily from the blade to the eye.)

A fireplace chimney showing how corbelling in the brick can give it a very nice design.

Using More Than One Flue

If more than one flue is needed, they can both be run in the same chimney. However, they must be separated by the thickness of a brick or block. Where this is impossible, put the tiles next to each other, but lay them so the joints are staggered one halfway up on the other. This will prevent an air leak in the joint of one from effecting the other. As you get to the top of the chimney, you will have to let one tile stick out further than the other to keep the draft of one from affecting the other.

Smoke Pipes

Before connecting smoke pipes to chimneys, check to see if the tile and the pipe are compatible. Your building supply or stove dealer can tell you what size pipe and tile you will need for the installation.

The pipe should enter the chimney at a flat horizontal line. It should not extend into the flue (just to the inside edge). The hole in the chimney should be filled around the pipe with fireclay. Viterous clay tile thimbles are made in different sizes to accept metal pipes and they should be used if possible.

The smoke pipe should not be very close to any combustible material. If you are within 18″ of a combustible surface, the pipe should be covered with a fireproof covering. If the pipe must pass through a partition made of wood or some other combustible material, either install a metal ventilating shield made for this purpose or box in the opening and put 8″ of brick work around the pipe. (Firebrick is best because regular brick transmits heat.)

When the weather is warm, smoke pipes should be taken down and cleaned or replaced if defective.

Chimneys run through an interior wall or ceiling should have 1″-2″ of clearance to allow movement from settling and temperature changes.

Flashing

Flashing made of copper or aluminum should be provided around the chimney where it passes through the roof. If the chimney is on a slanted roof, build a "cricket" behind the chimney to help shed ice and water from the upper side of the chimney.

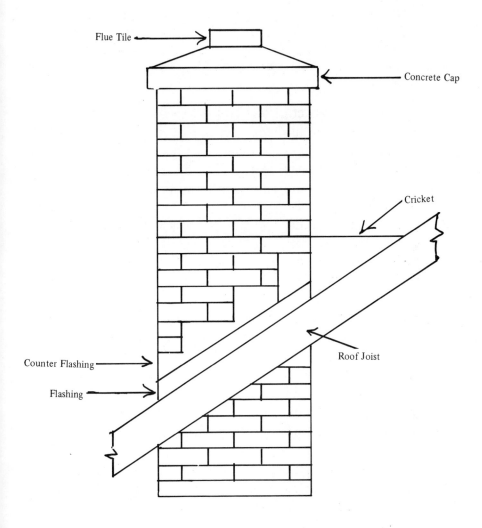

12

ANCHORS AND ADHESIVES

There are many types of anchors on the market that can be used in brick, block or concrete. The type of anchor you decide to use will depend on the material that you want to anchor and the weight of the material.

LEAD ANCHORS AND SCREWS - For light and medium anchoring in solid masonry, and concrete. This would include window installation, shelves, pipe and conduit straps and clamps, awnings, and signs.

For the best results the screw should protude ¼" past the end of the lead anchor. Screw length should equal the thickness of the material to be anchored plus the length of the anchor plus ¼".

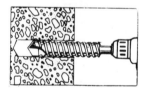 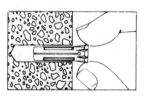 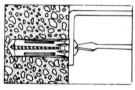

Drill a hole at least ¼" deeper than anchor length.

Insert anchor into the hole. If necessary tap the anchor to fit.

Insert screw through fixture and tighten. Wood screws can be used.

NYLON ANCHORS AND SCREW TYPE NAILS - For installation of drapery hardware and shelves, fix-

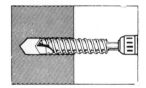 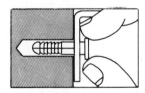 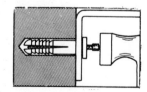

Drill hole slightly deeper than anchor length.

Insert anchor through fixture to be fastened. Tap anchor to fit flush.

Insert nail into anchor and tap with a hammer.

tures, wall brackets, and other household wall mount accessories, also electrical installations.

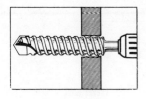

Drill a hole through the wall.

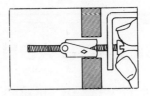

Put the bolt through the fixture; replace wings on bolt; push the wings in through the hole.

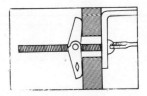

When the wings spread inside the wall, you tighten the bolt until the fixture is secure.

TOGGLE BOLTS - For anchoring in hollow walls and ceilings. You can anchor ceiling, wall fixtures of all types, electrical fixtures and heaters, storage racks, shelves, cabinets, partitions, pictures, hand rails, and bathroom fixtures.

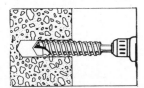

Drill a hole slightly deeper than the anchor length.

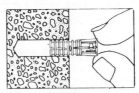

Insert the anchor into the hole. If necessary tap the anchor to fit flush.

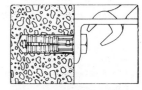

Insert the screw through the fixture into the anchor and tighten it securely.

LAG SHIELDS - These are for medium and heavy anchoring in solid masonry. Some typical applications are: wall fixtures of all types, heavy duty wall heating and cooling fixtures of all types, shelving, storage bins and racks, hand railings and construction of metal buildings.

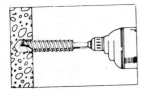

Drill a hole to anchor length.

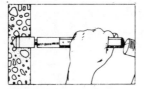

Set the anchor in with conical end down, flush with the surface. Place the tool on top of the anchor and set it with a hammer blow.

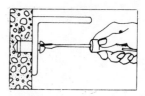

Place screw through the material and into the anchor; tighten securely.

CAULKING ANCHORS - For light and medium anchoring in solid materials. This would include windows, shelves, pipe and conduit straps and clamps, awnings, and signs. Can be used on most hard materials.

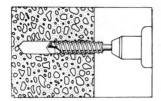

Drill a hole with a ¼" masonry drill (.260 - .270 Dia.) to 1 1/8" minimum depth.

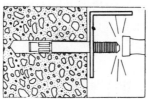

Tap the anchor into the hole through the material to be fastened.

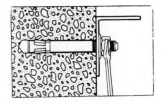

Place a washer on the stud and tighten the nut.

DROP IN STUD ANCHORS - For medium and heavy fastening in solid masonry. Typical applications would be in framing, wall fixtures of all types, heavy duty wall heating and cooling fixtures of all types, shelving, storage bins and racks, and hand railings.

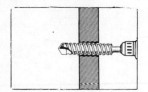

Drill a ¼" hole.

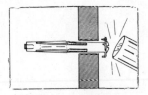

Insert anchor. A tap will set the three gripper teeth.

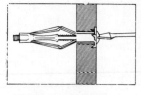

Tighten up the screw until it expands.

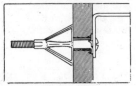

Remove screw, and place fixture over the anchor; reinsert screw and tighten.

HOLLOW WALL ANCHORS - For wall and ceiling fixtures of all types, wall and baseboard heating and cooling fixtures of all types, shelving, and storage bins and racks.

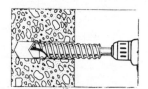

Drill a hole ¼"deeper than the anchor length; and clean the hole throughly.

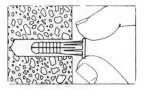

Insert the anchor into the hole. If it is necessary, tap the anchor to make it fit flush.

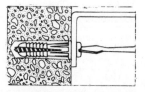

Insert the screw through the fixture to be fastened and tighten it into the anchor.

PLASTIC ANCHORS - For fastening drapery hardware, shelves, fixtures, and other light loads to masonry, such as brick, mortar, tile, and sheetrock. For best results, the screw must protrude ¼" through the bottom of the plastic anchor. Screw length should equal the thickness of the fixture plus the length of the plastic anchor plus ¼".

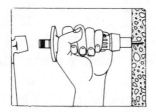

MASONRY FASTENING PINS - These are for fastening of wood and metal to masonry without drilling. The easiest way to install pins is to use a Diamond brand hammer. In using the pins, check to see if you are using the proper pin length for the project.

Locate and mark the entry point of the pin. Tap the pin slightly to begin the penetration. If you are using a Diamond brand tool, insert the pin into the tool and tap the tool lightly. Drive the fastener in with several solid hammer blows. In using a regular hammer, wear goggles to protect your eyes in case the pins fly out when struck. For proper pin size see the chart below.

For the Following Applications	In Concrete	In Cement Block	In New Cement or Mortar Joints	In Steel Up 3/16" Thick
		USE PIN LENGTH		
Wood 1/4" to 1/2" thick	1" - 1 1/4"	2"	1 1/4" - 1 1/2"	X
Wood 5/8" to 3/4"	1 1/2"	2" - 2 1/2"	1 1/2" - 2"	X
Wood 1 1/4" to 1 3/4"	2" - 2 1/2"	X	X	X
Steel up to 3/16" thick	X	X	X	3/4"

Adhesives

There is a large variety of adhesives on the market today. Many claim to be all-purpose adhesives that are made to bond a wide variety of materials together. There are also many adhesives made to bond just a very few types of materials together. You should pay close attention to the labels to see if the adhesive will bond the surface properly.

All adhesives require a clean surface to bond properly. Any oil or dirt will keep the adhesive from bonding to the surface properly. Some materials should be cleaned with a degreasing agent.

Try to match an adhesive to the job you are doing. With masonry, only a few types of adhesives work well. The adhesive that works the best is epoxy. All epoxys are fairly general in strength. In its original state, epoxy is somewhat like motor oil, and it will leak or drip out of a void or crack. Filled epoxys will solve this problem. The strength of epoxys is greater than the concrete or other masonry that it is applied to. (If you were to break up the masonry, you would find that the filled part of epoxy is stronger than either the concrete or the masonry.)

Epoxys consist of a two part formulation of resin and hardener. When they are mixed together in equal parts, they will bond like and unlike materials. Epoxys have excellent resistance to chemicals, salt water, gasoline, and oil.

Epoxys won't spread as easily in cold weather, but you can place them near heat to warm them before using. They can be used in any size batch that you can use in about 20 minutes. A small batch can be mixed with a stick and a couple of covers from small jars. When mixing a large batch, you can use an electric drill and a paint mixing blade. An artist's spatula with a 3″ blade or a paring knife with the point ground off both make excellent tools for epoxy. A piece of screen wire or a piece of fiberglass cloth make filling large holes easier. A patch can be painted the next day. For smoothing out work, dip the tool you are using in alcohol or lacquer thinner and smooth out the work. A piece of wax paper placed over the patch will permit you to mould or shape it better. Remove the wax paper about the time that the patch is cured. The cure will vary with thickness and temperature. A thickness of $1/16''$ will cure in about 8 hours at room temperature. A thickness of $1/4''$ in 6 hours and a thickness of $1''$ in about 4 hours. Heat may be applied to make it cure faster, though most work is ready for service after about 24 hours. A filled epoxy will allow you to work on overhead jobs since it won't drip or sag from the cracks. A good filled epoxy is PC-7

P.V.A.'s (poly vinyl acetate) such as Elmer's glue, Duro, and other white glues, when mixed one part P.V.A. with 4 parts water, to which is added regular cement and sand, makes a far stronger bond than a regular cement mix, though in no way comparable to the strength of regular or filled epoxy.

Styrene-Butadiene is a thick paste that is ready to use from the container and can be applied from a tube on small jobs or with a putty knife on larger surfaces. It doesn't set up fast, sometimes taking two days or longer. Styrene-Butadiene is good for installing bolts in holes in masonry and for reparing loose tiles in bathrooms and kitchens. Once it hardens, it can be drilled, sanded, and painted. It is like epoxy in that it is waterproof.

Concrete adhesives are made by many companies, and one of the best is made by the Franklin Glue Company, called Franklin Concrete Adhesive. It is a polymeric resin composition designed to act as a coat between new cement, new concrete or new plaster and old surfaces of wood, stone, and cement. When added to Portland cement or concrete, it will give resilience and toughness with substantially reduced cracking. It makes feather edging much easier. Spread it on surfaces that are thoroughly cleaned, without diluting it. Once it becomes tacky, it is ready for the new cement to be applied. The best results will be obtained if the new cement is poured in less than two hours after the glue becomes tacky. Another way to use this adhesive is to add one or two gallons of it to a 94 pound bag of Portland cement and the regular amount of sand. Dilute the adhesive with the mixing water just before using it. Use the cement in the usual fashion and cure it in the same manner as a regular batch.

13

CLEANING MASONRY SURFACES

Masonry cleaning products should always be handled with care. Rubber gloves, goggles and protective clothing should be worn so as to avoid splashing the skin and eyes. The entire label on each container should be read prior to use.

There are different masonry cleaners on the market. I've always had good luck with products made by the Process Solvent Company. The following are some cleaners and how to use them.

VANA-TROL--This cleaner is used to clean light colored brick, stone, structural tile, exposed aggregate and other new masonry. It comes in a liquid formula of organic acids and special wetting systems. The proper way to use Vana-Trol is to prewet all masonry surfaces with water, apply the cleaning solution at a ratio of 8 parts water to 1 part Vana-Trol. Use a masonry scrub brush. Let the solution soak for 2-3 minutes, then thoroughly rinse with as much water as possible. It can be bought in gallons and quarts.

The above cleaner will also clean "efflorescence" or white scum, which is caused by insoluable salts and moisture coming to the surface.

NO. 101 LIME SOLVENT--If you want to clean red brick, concrete block and other dark colored new masonry, use No. 101 Lime Solvent. This solvent is a

combination of inorganic and organic acids with che-
lating and wetting agents. The proper way to use No.
101 Lime Solvent is to pre-wet surfaces with water, apply the prepared solution in a ratio of 4 parts water to 1
part solvent. Scrape off the excess mortar and re-apply
the solution. Rinse the cleaned area very thoroughly
with water. It comes in quarts and gallons, a gallon
covering 400 sq. ft.

RESTORATION CLEANER--By ProSoCo Inc. is
ideal to clean old masonry surfaces. It will remove carbon (aging stain) from brick and tile surfaces, rust and
mud stains from brick, tile and concrete and paint oxidation from masonry surfaces around painted window
frames, gutters and aluminum siding. For removing aging stains (carbon), use in the concentrated form or
dilute 3 parts water to 1 part solvent, depending on the
severity of the stains. To apply, pre-wet the area to be
cleaned. Apply the moisture with a soft, fiber brush or
roller. Soak 3-5 minutes. Re-apply the cleaner and rinse
with clean water, using as much water as possible. For
removing rust and mud stains, dilute the mix 3-1 or use
it straight if needed. Prewet the area to be cleaned and
apply the mixture liberally with a stiff bristled brush.
Let it soak for 3-5 minutes and re-apply the mix if
necessary. Rinse the area with as much water as possible. To clean paint oxidation, use the same procedure
as for rust and mud stains. Restoration cleaner covers
200 sq. ft. Restoration Cleaner is available in quarts
and gallons.

LIMESTONE RESTORER--Limestone stains usually come from carbon, dirt, algae and other atmospheric
contaminants. This cleaner is a heavy duty liquid
cleaner made of a heavily inhibited blend of inorganic
and organic acids with special wetting agents. To apply,
dilute in 2 parts water to 1 part cleaner. Brush liberally

on the surface. Let it soak for 2 or 3 minutes. Rinse the surface with a high pressure water spray. Limestone Restorer can be bought in gallons.

DEGREASER AND ETCH - When the problem is heavy, deepset oil and grease stains in concrete floors and driveways. Use Degreaser and Etch. Mix Degreaser and Etch, 1 part concentrate and 2 parts water. Pre-wet the concrete to be cleaned. Apply the cleaning solution liberally with a masonry cleaning brush. Let it soak for 2 to 3 minutes. Re-apply and scrub vigorously. Rinse thoroughly with clean water. It can be used in the concentrated form on an extremely dirty floor. It covers 125 sq. ft. Degreaser and Etch can also be used to prepare a concrete floor for surface coating. Dilute the cleaner 1 part concentrate to 3 parts water. Pre-wet the area and apply the cleaning solution liberally with a masonry washing brush. Soak 3-4 minutes. Rinse the area with clean water. Heavily stained areas may require re-application of the cleaner and more scrubbing. Degreaser and Etch is available in gallons.

MASONRY PAINT STRIPPER AND RESTORATION CLEANER--If the problem you have is removing graffiti and layers of chipped, peeling paint from masonry surfaces, use Masonry Paint Stripper and Restoration Cleaner. To use it correctly you should apply it directly to graffiti or painted masonry surfaces. Allow the material to remain on the surface for 30 minutes to two hours, depending on the thickness and type of paint. Throughly rinse with as much water pressure as possible. After washing, use Restoration Cleaner to neutralize any paint stripper left on the surface. A gallon will cover 75 sq. ft.

DRIVEWAY CLEANER --For removing oil and grease and traffic stains without etching concrete use Driveway Cleaner. Pour the material directly from the container on the surface to be cleaned. Scrub the cleaner into the surface pores using a scrub brush. Let it soak for 5 to 7 minutes. Rinse it thoroughly with as much water as possible.

Removing smoke and soot stains from around fireplaces and stoves can be done with Driveway Cleaner. Apply the cleaner directly from the container to the surface to be cleaned. Let it soak for 2 to 3 minutes. Rinse thoroughly with a wet rag or sponge.

ASPHALT AND TAR REMOVER -- Made by the ProSoCo, Inc. is excellent for removal of asphalt, tar, grease, oil and other hard to remove stains from brick, stone and other masonry surfaces. It can also be used to clean equipment. Used in concentrated form, it is a quick acting cleaner. It contains special emulsifiers and wetting agents. It is non-corrosive and non-caustic. Apply liberally to dry surfaces. Allow it to set several minutes. Re-apply and scrub stained area. Rinse thoroughly with fresh water. One gallon covers 75 sq. ft.

GROUT CLEANER -- Made for the removal of excess grout on quarry tile, brick and slate floors. Also, for removal of acid scum on the above materials. It is a non-hydrochloric acid liquid compound. It contains strong inorganic acids, special wetting systems and other surface active materials. To apply, pre-wet the area to be cleaned, apply diluted solution. Let stand 1 to 3 minutes. Re-apply solution, scrub vigorously. Sponge or mop surface and rinse with fresh water.

14

STONE

Many people think that stone is the most beautiful of all building materials. Stone houses and houses with stone veneer on them are few and far between. Since these buildings were usually built with local stone, they are next to impossible to duplicate. The cost of stone today usually prevents people from building complete homes with it and they usually just settle for some decorative veneer on the front wall. Originally, stone was cleared from the land and drawn to a building site on flat bed sleds by a team of horses. This stone was called "field stone" for obvious reasons. Farmers would also erect stone fences; and many of these still stand today. Stone masonry became an art, since masons had to cut and shape the stone themselves when building homes. Many of the cut stone buildings of a hundred years ago are monuments to the men who spent weeks and months building them.

Stone quarrys came along with the building of towns. Since there were no concrete building blocks then, and brick usually had to be shipped in by railroad cars, stone and wood were the main building materials. Most of the larger stone quarries are still active today and it is possible to buy stone for projects around the home, large or small.

Patios

For building a patio, a flagstone can be bought in thicknesses from ⅝″ up to 2″ and in dimensions from 12″ × 12″ up to 24″ × 36″, allowing you a large selection of sizes to choose from to fit the area you plan to cover. Measure the area and draw a plan on how you would like the patio to look and you will be able to judge whether you want all 12″ × 12″ × ⅝″ thick or a larger thicker pattern. You might want to use a thicker 1½″ or 2″ stone where something heavy might go over the surface, possibly causing a crack. For example: a 12″ × 12″ and a 24″ × 24″ can be used together to get a two against one pattern.

You might want to buy what is called irregular flagging, usually bought by the ton, in 1″ or 1½″ thick and 1″ to 3″ square pieces. Doing this will allow a lot of combinations.

Let's assume you want to build a patio 8′ × 16′. It could be laid out as shown here.

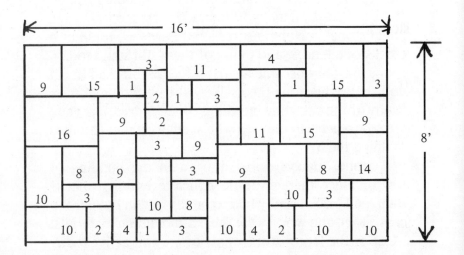

The stone use for this patio would be as follows:

Piece	No. of Pieces Required	Length"	Width"
1	4	11 ½	11 ½
2	5	11 ½	17 ½
3	8	11 ½	23 ½
4	3	11 ½	29 ½
8	3	17 ½	17 ½
9	6	17 ½	23 ½
10	7	17 ½	29 ½
11	2	17 ½	35 ½
14	1	23½	23 ½
15	3	23 ½	29 ½
16	1	23 ½	35 ½

The base for the patio should be four inches of gravel and two inches of sand. Save enough sand for setting the stones. After the stones are put down, they should be leveled. This is sometimes easier if you level each stone as you lay it. Look over the situation, and make your decision now as to whether you want a slope or a flat level patio, and lay the stones accordingly. The slope should be slight and away from the home. Sand should be brushed into the joints between the stones and then wet with a spray from a hose to settle the sand. If you do this two or three times you will fill the space between the stones enough to keep them from sliding.

Stone Treads

On the edge of your patio or on stone steps you might want to use what is called stone treads. These treads can be bought in a natural finish or cut to exact sizes by sawing or shaping them.

Natural stone is stone that was formed parallel to the stratification in the ground by the earth's movements.

Natural stone finishes are usually called "quarry treads." They usually come in 12", 14", 16", and 18" widths, 3" to 8" lengths and 1" to 2½" thicknesses. They have the natural stone finish on the top and bottom and usually have snapped edges which carry a natural finish.

Another kind of tread is the milled or sawed tread. These treads are cut from a large stone by diamond saws. Some of the original stones are 6" square. They are put on large tables and sawed with a wire saw or a long straight blade saw. The pieces that are sawed off are then sawed again into smaller tread size pieces. Sawing or milling the stone gives it a smooth surface on all sides. Sawed stone can be cut to exact measurements.

Sawn stone is sometimes used in sills under doors or windows in combination with other masonry. These sills are cut in 1½" to 2" thicknesses and in lengths from 3" to 6". It would be wise to buy your sills before you build and make the openings fit the sill as you are building.

Stone Veneer

Stone veneer can be put over many sound surfaces, but will require a footing or foundation because of the weight. Veneer is usually sold in 3" or 4" wide pieces. Natural Bed veneer comes in pieces 1½" to 6" high and in random lengths. This is close to what is found in many older stone veneer walls.

Making Patterns

To make a pattern, you will need what is called "multiple rise veneer." These veneer stones come split face and seam face and they are usually sold in one and two ton bundles. In a typical bundle, you would find about 15% 2¼" thick, 50% 5" thick, and 35% 7¾" thick. These percentages allow you to lay a stone veneer in what is called coursed, broken bond, and ashlar bond walls. These bonds are pictured later.

Stone is usually sold by the square foot or by the ton. Veneer is sold by the ton. Note that thinner flagstone and veneer stone will come with more pieces per ton. (About 250 sq. ft. of ⅝" multiple pattern flagstone is equal to 70 sq. ft. of 2" thick flagstone.) It should also be remembered that the thicker the stone, the more weight it will support.

When you buy veneer stone you can specify if you want it all in one thickness. It will, however, cost more for the 2¼" and less for the 5" and 7¾" sizes. The problem with only one size is that you loose the flexibility of forming different bonds and designs.

Retaining Wall Stone

If you would like to construct a retaining wall, buy what is called "retaining wall stone." It is much cheaper than cut veneer but varies greatly in size, allowing you to build what are called uncoursed or random coursed rubble walls. Always remember: cut stone and special orders raise the price.

Undressed Stone

If you are getting your stone out of a field or from an old stone wall, you will probably be coming home with what is called undressed or rustic rubble. You will need a hammer and a stone chisel to finish off the rough edges.

Using the chisel, first mark the surface that is to be cut by scraping it with the edge of the chisel or marking it with a pencil. Use light blows and move the chisel slowly along the line, after each blow. Go back and

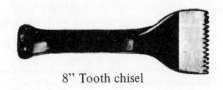

8" Tooth chisel

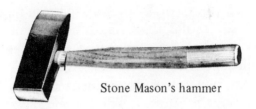

Stone Mason's hammer

forth. You might break the stone into pieces or you might make a perfect cut. It takes stone masons years of working with stone to know exactly where and when a stone will break. Work slowly and you might be lucky.

When cutting with a hammer and chisel always wear a pair of safety goggles to protect your eyes from stone or metal chips.

Cutting with a Saw

One way of getting a straight cut is to use a masonry cut off blade. Mark the line to be cut with a pencil and cut slowly and carefully, remembering that there will be dust fragments of stone flying from the blade. Hold the piece that is to be cut in some sort of jig to keep it from flying away when the saw starts cutting. Watch your hands.

Stone Can Be Drilled

Stone can be drilled with a carbide tipped masonry

bit. These bits come in various sizes and can be bought in hardware stores. They work easier with a slow speed drill. First drill then blow away the dust and drill again, keeping the residue away from the hole.

Stone Foundations

If you decide to build a stone foundation for your house, you will need a large quantity of stone. It would be to your advantage to have an old foundation or stone wall to use for a supply.

First pour a footing to begin the wall on. (consult the earlier chapters). The footing for a stone foundation will depend on how wide your wall is going to be, but the wall should be at least 16″ wide and the footing 24″ wide and 8″ thick. You might be able to build a thinner wall, but it wouldn't carry as much weight and would be harder to construct because of the odd sizes of stone you will be using.

Most flat stones can be used for your foundation, but always remember that you should have a bond stone. A bond stone is one which extends through the wall from one side to the other, and is used every two feet or so in each direction, to tie the wall together.

To save yourself extra mortar, use small stones to fill in the gaps between the larger ones. When you put mortar on the wall, it will bond all the stones large and small, and leave less holes or voids to fill with mortar. A side benefit is in the elimination of voids where water can collect and freeze causing a damage.

The construction of a stone foundation can take much longer than one built with concrete blocks. It will require more labor and more sand and cement. But for the handyman who has the time and patience and *most of all* enough stone on his property, it can be cheaper than blocks or poured concrete.

RUBBLE STONE MASONRY

1   Random rubble masonry

2   Coursed rubble masonry

Points to Remember

A stone foundation wall using mortar will have to be built with stones that are clean and free of moss and dirt in order for the mortar to stick. A simple washing with clean water will do the trick.

Mortar should be mixed a little at a time since the wall is built more slowly than a block wall. If you are using a wheelbarrow, mix six shovels of sand and two of mortar cement with just enough water to mix the materials to a workable but not soupy mix. If you add too much water let the mix set a while, it might dry up enough by itself. If you need it right away, add half a shovel of sand. If you need more than the half shovel of sand to stiffen the mix, add cement along with it in a 3 sand to 1 cement ratio. By keeping the mortar stiff you can keep it from running down over the face of the wall where it would be hard to clean off.

If there are holes in the wall after you have laid some of it up, you can use some stiff mortar and a pointing trowel or tuck pointer to fill the holes.

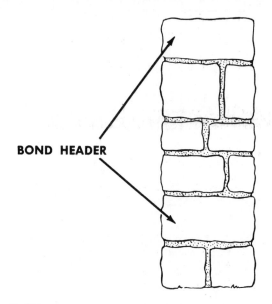

BOND HEADER

Rubble stone masonry wall showing bonding stone.

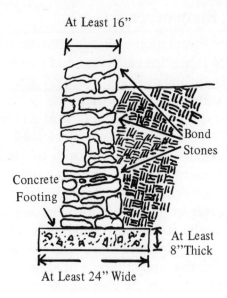

At Least 16"

Bond Stones

Concrete Footing

At Least 8" Thick

At Least 24" Wide

Stone Foundation

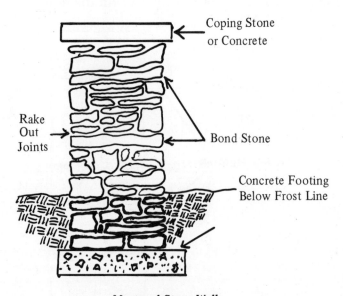

Coping Stone or Concrete

Rake Out Joints

Bond Stone

Concrete Footing Below Frost Line

Mortared Stone Wall

This wall is of uncoursed rubble. The mortar joints have been raked out to show the characteristics of the stone.

This wall is of uncoursed rubble but with flush joints. The stone used in this wall is flat and relatively smooth. The mortar is light-colored.

This retaining wall is built out of random coursed rubble. Notice how the stones are level at the top and the bond is broken frequently.

This is a dressed or hammer cut stone wall. The bond is Ashlar, two against one. This particular wall required a mason with patience.

This wall is laid in random coursed broken Ashlar. The light-colored stones were cut in a quarry. The dark mortar sets off the stone. You will notice that there are two different sizes here: 2½" and 5".

This chimney is built of a variety of stone sizes. The bond is broken bond Ashlar, 2 against 1 and 3 against 1. It is made using dark mortar and raked joints.

This wall was made from quarry stone. The stones were probably left over from cuttings. This is broken bond Ashlar.

This is a cobble stone veneer. The stone on the top is a quarry coping stone, cut to size. The base at each end is made of concrete. The stones at the corners are cut and trimmed.

This is a veneer wall using stone that is nearly all the same size. The wall is called coursed Ashlar. The bed joints are all level and the end joints are staggered, making it a strong wall.

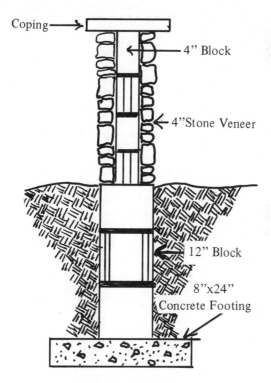

Coping

4" Block

4" Stone Veneer

12" Block

8"x24"
Concrete Footing

Veneered Stone Wall

This is a dry stone wall—in this case, a retaining wall. The stones used here are mostly flat. The top stones are the full width of the wall, and two and three feet long. Water drains through this type of wall due to the lack of mortar.

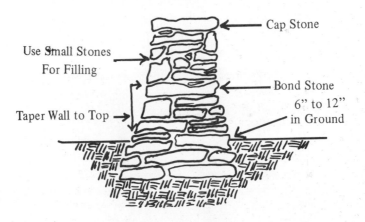

Cap Stone

Use Small Stones For Filling

Bond Stone 6" to 12" in Ground

Taper Wall to Top

Dry Stone Wall

The corner of this old building is made of quarry stone and brick. The brick bond is Flemish, and the stone is coursed Ashlar. This wall was built in 1894.

This building was built in 1818. The construction started, the stone used was different from that used to finish it. Note the difference just below the windows.

Glossary

American bond The bond in which a header course occurs every seventh course.

Aggregates The materials (sand and gravel) mixed with Portland cement to make concrete.

Anchor bolt A bolt set into masonry (to secure a board or a piece of metal to the masonry) to a given height when the masonry is soft.

Angle iron A piece of steel in the shape of a 90° angle. It is usually used to hold brick or other masonry above an opening.

Ashlar A type of stonework. Usually stone cut in square or rectangular shapes. Coursed Ashlar would be stones that are laid in level bed joints.

Backfill The operation of replacing dirt removed in excavation.

Batter The slope of a face of the wall in a backwards direction. It would be opposite the overhang.

Batter-
boards   Boards, in pairs, nailed to stakes a short distance behind each corner to hold the building lines for grading and laying out the buildings.

Backing
up   The process of laying the inside portion of a cavity wall.

Bearing   The surface of a wall where a lintel or another wall sets.

Bearing
wall   A wall which supports part of the structure.

Bed   (1) The flat surface of a stone parallel to its stratification.
(2) The horizontal courses of mortar on which masonry is laid.

Bench
mark   A mark or point accurately obtained with a builder's level on an immovable object.

Bond   (1) The overlapping of masonry units to make a wall stronger and to make the wall pleasing in appearance.
(2) The reaction of mortar when applied to masonry surfaces.

Bond
stones   Stones that run through the width of a wall to hold it together.

Broken range	Usually applied to stonework. It is the breaking of the bond at frequent points.
Brick veneer	Walls that are brick on a frame made of wood or block.
Butter	To spread mortar on the end of a brick or block before laying it in the wall.
Cavity wall	A wall that has a space between the outside face and the interior wall; an airspace.
Cap	A cement finish on the top of a chimney to make a chimney shed water.
Cement	A mixture of clay and limestone ground to make mortar and concrete.
Cement plaster	A mix of Portland cement and sand used as a finished coat.
Closure	The last brick or block laid in a wall to finish a course.
Coping	The top course of masonry to finish the top of a wall. It is made to keep water out of the wall.
Course	Each layer of block, brick, or stone laid to a certain height.

Corbel | A horizontal course of masonry projecting past the last course and used to support the next course.

Cricket | A small structure built on the upper side of a chimney between the chimney and the roof, on which flashing is placed.

Dry stone wall | A type of stone wall that is built without mortar.

Darby | A large float, used to smooth the surface of a freshly poured piece of concrete. Made of wood or metal, 42″ long.

Dressed stone | The stone used for walls, after it has been squared by using a hammer and stone chisel.

Efflorescence | The appearance of a white powder on the surface of stone or brick walls. The white powder is caused by soluble salts in the mortar, and sometimes in the brick, drawn out by the heat from the sun.

English bond | The brick bond that consists of alternate courses of headers and stretchers.

Excavate | The process of digging out a foundation.

Expansion joint | A joint in masonry construction to allow

for expansion and contraction due to temperature changes

Face brick   A well burned brick used for exterior work, uniform in appearance and dimension.

Fat   In concrete work, the term used to refer to the cement brought to the surface by floating the slab.

Fat mortar   A mixture of cement and sand that is very sticky due to an insufficient amount of sand.

Fieldstone   Rough, uncut stones as they are picked from a field.

Firebrick   Special brick made for the inside of a fireplace or furnace.

Fireclay   A heat resistant clay that will not soften or burn up. It is used for laying firebrick.

Flagstones   Stone in sizes from $\frac{5}{8}''$ to $2''$ thick and $1'$ to $2' \times 3'$ used in sidewalks.

Flashing   Strips of metal (tin, copper or aluminum) used to keep water from leaking around a chimney, window or door.

Flemish bond   The laying of brick, using a whole brick, then a half, then a whole, etc. The half brick (headers) are centered over the whole brick (stretchers).

Flue — The passage in a chimney through which smoke and gases escape from the house.

Flue tile — A hollow tile 24″ long used in the construction of chimneys. They are made of viterous clays and aren't affected by heat or gases from a fire.

Footing — The base of a wall. Constructed of concrete, twice as wide as the wall it will carry and as thick as the width of the wall. Example: An 8″ block wall will need a footing that is 8″ thick and 16″ wide.

Form — The mold used to shape concrete. Forms are made of wood or metal, because of the pressure against them.

Foundation — The basement and underground portion of a building; the part of construction that supports the structure.

Frost line — The depth that frost is driven into the ground during the coldest months of the year. Usually given as an average.

Glazed tile — Tile that has a glass-like finish on the surface.

Glazed brick — Like tile with a glass-like finish on the surface.

Glass blocks — Blocks of transparent glass fused together

in roughly 4″ widths for use in building windows and walks.

Grade   The slope of the ground around a building.

Grout   A thin mortar used in an almost liquid consistency, to fill joints and cavities solidly.

Header   In brickwork, the end of a brick showing in the face of a wall.

Hearth   The portion of a fireplace on which the fire is built. An extended hearth is built past the face of the fireplace. A raised hearth is built above the level of the floor.

Herring-
bone bond   When brick are laid in a zig-zag pattern in a patio or walk.

Jamb   The sides of a door, window or other opening.

Jointer   The tool used to make a masonry joint in mortar. Jointers come in many sizes and styles.

Lime   Produced by burning limestone in a kiln long enough to drive off the carbon dioxide. The base for mortar.

Lintel   A horizontal support for masonry, usually an angle iron.

Mantel   A shelf over the fireplace opening, usually for ornamental reasons. It is sometimes built into the masonry.

Mortar   A mixture of sand and cement. It can be made different ways by using lime, Portland cement and sand, or mortar cement and sand.

Mortar
board   A square board used to hold mortar for a mason.

Mud   Mortar.

Natural
bed   The surface of a stone, parallel to its stratification.

Neat
cement   When Portland cement is mixed with water, but with no sand or lime.

Pargetting   A thin coat of mortar used to smooth out rough insides of brick or stonework, sometimes in preparation for waterproofing.

Party
walls   A partition between two properties.

Pitch   To use a chisel to square stone. A stone chisel.

Pier   A vertical section of brick or other

masonry used to hold an arch or carry beams and girders.

Pilaster	A pier built in a wall to strengthen a wall against horizontal forces. Projects ⅓ to ½ the width of the wall.
Plinth course	The projecting course of masonry-- usually called the water table. Located at the first floor level.
Plumb	To be perpendicular to a given point. Straight up and down.
Plumbline	To extend a line plumb from the top to the bottom of a building.
Plumb bob	A weight attached to a line used to establish a plumb point on a surface.
Pointing	The process of filling in joints after masonry has set.
Pointing trowel	A small trowel in the shape of a mason's trowel, used for filling in small holes and for pointing up work.
Portland cement	A cement that is used primarily in concrete, made of limestone, clay and other ingredients that are mixed, burned and ground to powder.

Pumice
stone   A fine stone ground for use in polishing.

Quarry   A rock bed. A place where rock is cut and
            sold in sizes.

Queen
closer   A brick cut in half lengthwise.

Quoins   Projecting courses of brickwork at cor-
            ners for ornamental reasons.

Racking   Building ends of walls in steps, to make
            continuing work easier.

Rake joint To remove some of the mortar from a
            joint to a uniform depth, before it sets.

Range
work   When laying stone, to continue to lay the
            stone across the length of a wall, even
            though the courses aren't all the same
            thickness. Sometimes called coursed
            Ashlar.

Rein-
forced
concrete   Concrete constructed with metal bars or
            wire in the concrete to give it more tensel
            strength.

Retaining
wall   A wall of masonry used to keep dirt or
            other material from falling.

Rowlock course	When bricks are laid on edge in a wall showing the end of the brick.
Rubble	Stone as it comes from the field or quarry, not dressed or cut.
Running bond	The same as a plain stretcher bond, when only stretchers are used.
Scarify	To make scratches in the first coat of cement so another coat will bond better.
Screed	A board, usually 2″ × 4″, used to strike off the concrete level with the forms.
Scutch	A tool that looks like a pick, only smaller, used to trim masonry.
Skintled brick-work	Brick laid with alternate bricks projecting out of the face.
Slush joint	To throw mortar in a joint after the bricks are laid.
Smoke chamber	The portion of a fireplace above the damper, sloped to meet the flue.
Soldier course	A course of brick laid with the brick standing on edge with the thin side on the face.

Spall   When a piece of masonry chips off the main part.

Splay   A slope at the side of a window or door.

Story pole A pole on which courses are marked to keep corners at the same height.

Stretcher A brick or block laid lengthwise in a wall.

Struck
joint   A joint that has been made by pressing the mortar with a trowel.

Structural
steel   Steel lintels, beams or columns used in construction of buildings.

Stucco   Cement or plaster put on the exterior of walls, which when painted is water resistant.

Tempering Adding water to mortar to soften it to its original consistency.

Terra
cotta   Baked clay of a very good quality, used for ornamental work.

Throat   The opening in a fireplace where the damper is located.

Tile   Flat pieces of clay burned and many times glazed for floors, walls and areas where frequent washing is needed.

Toothing   Building the end of a wall so that the end of each alternate course of brick or block is laid in half way past the last course.

Trig   When a brick or block is laid in the center of the wall to hold the line from sagging or blowing, and to help keep the wall plumb.

Tuck
pointing   Filling in joints in masonry with mortar by using a tool called a tuck pointer, which come in different sizes.

Vermicu-
lated   Usually referred to as hard-baked clay.

Wall tie   A thin piece of metal used to hold veneered work to the surface to which it is applied.

Weephole   A hole left in the bottom of a masonry wall to allow water to have a place to escape from the inside of the wall.

Wind
shelf   The ledge behind the damper and directly beneath the flue.

PROJECTS

PROJECTS

PLANTER

Tools:
bricklayer's trowel
4″ hand level
bottomless wooden box
framing square
hammer
pointing tool
broad-bladed brick chisel

Materials:
about 15 solid brick units (have a
few more handy) for each planter
small amount premixed mortar
(one 60-pound bag will do 3
planters, including allowance
for waste)
nylon rope or plastic tubing

Have handy:
shovel
wheelbarrow
garden hose
garden hoe
hand brush

Outdoor brick planters can add a touch of charm
to the most modest of gardens and will provide hours of
enjoyment for the family "green thumb."

Material estimates above are for the brick planter
pictured and described here. The ambitious gardener
may wish to change the size and shape of a planter and,

of course, adjustments in material needs must then be considered.

This planter works best when laid on a concrete base. Lay brick in place with mortar as shown, adding "weep holes"—nylon rope or plastic tubes—in the vertical joints in the first course of brick. After the mortar has hardened—about a week—spread a layer of gravel in the planter to allow for good drainage.

PEDESTAL

Tools:
>   wooden float
>   trowel

Materials:
>   30 solid brick units (have a few
>   extra on hand)
>   ½ cubic foot concrete (1 bag
>   premixed concrete)

Have handy:
>   shovel
>   wheelbarrow
>   garden hoe

This brick pedestal, designed to provide a dramatic setting for your favorite flower arrangement, is so easy to build you may just want to supervise and let the children have fun creating your new garden addition.

Because no mortar is used in its construction, it is important to have a level, stable base for the pedestal. Gravel may be used, but a concrete slab is best. The slab should be 16″ × 12″ square and about 4″ thick. Make sure the footing is excavated deep enough to go below the frost line.

Place the brick as shown. As you go along, lay each course so that the brick units overlay the cracks between the units on the level below.

MORTARLESS PAVING:
walkway, patio, driveway and steps

Tools:
> mason's string
> hand level
> 2″ or 4″ hand level
> brick chisel
> wooden tamper
> wooden screed board
> mason's pointing tool
> trowel

Materials:
> brick, sand, cement, gravel (consult
>   estimating tables)
> mortar for restraining edges
> roofing felt to fit area

Have handy:
> shovel
> wheelbarrow
> garden hose
> garden rake
> broom
> garden hoe

Brick walkways, driveways and steps have long
been a feature of formal estates, and can add the same
touch of elegance to your home. You can apply these
principles of mortarless brickwork to anything from a
small patio to a driveway. The scope of the project is up
to you.

A concrete foundation is best for mortarless brick installations; because no mortar is used, the base should be as level and stable as possible. Alternatively, a gravel base about 4″ deep, under a 1″ layer of stone screenings or graded pea gravel, may be used. A 1″ to 2″ sand cushion is an economical but less durable choice. If the installation is shaded and likely to be damp at times, it's a good idea to lay 15-pound roofing felt over the base before laying your brick; this will prevent the "greening" effect which occurs when algae grow. It also makes the bricklaying process easier on your knees.

Another drainage consideration is slope; make sure you have a slope of at least ¼″ per foot for good drainage.

Begin by installing a restraining edge of brick around the edges of the walkway, set in concrete or mortar. These brick should be laid flat with the longest dimension horizontal and the face parallel to the edge. This restraining edge is necessary because mortarless brick tend to shift at the edges. No restraining is necessary where paving can be abutted to existing curbs or structures. If moisture accumulation might be a problem, put "weep holes" of plastic tubing or nylon rope wick in the joints.

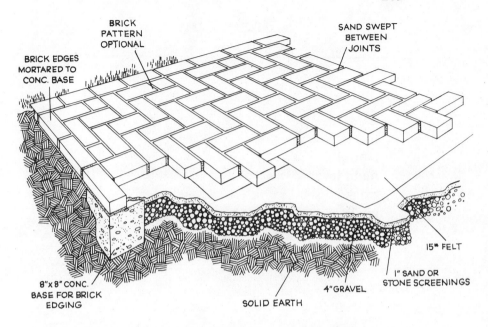

BRICK
PATTERN
OPTIONAL

SAND SWEPT
BETWEEN
JOINTS

BRICK EDGES
MORTARED TO
CONC. BASE

15" FELT

8"x 8" CONC.
BASE FOR BRICK
EDGING

SOLID EARTH

4" GRAVEL

1" SAND OR
STONE SCREENINGS

Lay out the brick according to your selected pattern. Sweep sand or a mixture of three parts sand to one part Portland cement over the walkway surface when completed and wash down with the garden hose.

To create a walkway on sloping ground, use railroad ties treated with preservative. They may be laid directly on dirt. You may substitute well-staked 2″ × 4″ redwood planks for the restraining edges; it is advisable to slope the brick areas slightly to either side to allow for drainage.

Barbecue

Tools:
    hammer
    mason's string
    trowel
    hand level
    brick chisel
    chalk
    wooden float
    hand brush

Materials:
    450 cored brick units $3\frac{3}{4}'' \times 2\frac{1}{4}'' \times 8''$
    75 solid brick units, same
        dimensions
    6 cubic feet of mortar
    27 cubic feet concrete for
        foundation
    $1\frac{2}{3}$ cubic feet concrete for
        hearthslab
    20 reinforcing bars $\frac{3}{8}''$ in diameter:
    5 bars 18'' long
    3 bars 32'' long
    12 bars 4'' long

Siting a barbecue is a matter of convenience to the cook. It is wise, however, to take notice of prevailing winds; you don't want smoke to blow directly into your windows or those of a neighbor.

Sand-finish brick is a good choice for reducing cleanup work after the job because mortar won't stick or smear, although crumbs will still have to be brushed away.

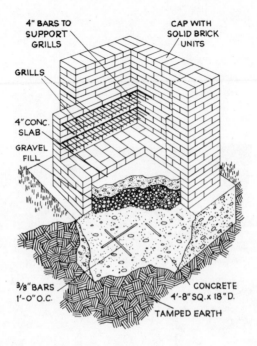

Excavate and pour the concrete foundation to the dimensions indicated, placing reinforcing bars as shown. Crisscross the bars in a grid pattern and prop them up with brick units so that they lay approximately in the center. If you prefer, they can be wired together and handled as a unit.

Draw the outline of the barbecue on the foundation slab, leaving at least 2″ all around. Lay out the first two courses of brick to see if the pattern works allowing ½″ for where the mortar joints will be.

Build the corners first, going three or four courses high, then filling in the wall from corner to corner. The bottom course should be bonded to the slab with mortar. Use a hand level frequently to keep the wall plumb and the rows of brick level.

Excess mortar may be clipped off with the trowel two or three rows at a time. As soon as the mortar is "thumbprint" hard, use a mason's pointing tool to shape and compress the mortar between brick.

As construction proceeds, insert 4″ lengths of reinforcing bars in the mortar joints to support the grills as shown.

Use solid brick units for the top of the barbecue walls.

Excess crumbs of mortar which remain when the wall is finished may be brushed away with a soft fiber hand brush.

Retaining wall

Tools:
> bricklayer's trowel
> mason's string
> mason's hand level
> 2″ and 4″ hand levels
> framing square
> mason's pointing tool
> wooden float

Materials:
> 1310 brick 3¾″ × 2¼″ × 8″ per 100
>   square feet of wall
> 44 brick 3¾″ × 2¼″ × 8″ per foot of
>   wall length
> 20 cubic feet of mortar per 100
>   square feet of wall
> 2.33 cubic feet of concrete per
>   foot of wall length
> ⅜″ steel reinforcing bars, 52″ long,
>   bent 9″ from one end at 90° angle — one for
>   every 3½ feet of wall length.
> 2 10″ pieces of prefabricated joint
>   reinforcement for 8″ wide wall
>   for every 9½ feet of wall length
> ⅜″ steel reinforcing bars, 18″ long,
>   one for every 3½ feet of wall
>   length.
> ½″ steel bars for length of footing
>   (allow 10″ lapping splice)
> plastic tubing
> small amount asphalt

Have handy:
  shovel
  wheelbarrow
  garden hose
  garden rake
  hammer
  old broom (short, stiff bristles)

Brick retaining walls protect your property while enhancing its appearance. When a cut is made in a hillside, escaping mositure will eventually erode it into a slope. Retaining walls prevent this erosion by holding moisture in the ground.

This is an ambitious project and calls for particularly good workmanship. Remember to comply with local building codes. This wall is to be built no more than 3″ high. Study the diagram and refer to it frequently.

Dig excavation as indicated. Use some loose brick to lay the bottom reinforcing bars on. Wire the vertical bar to the bottom bar and prop in place. Insert remain-

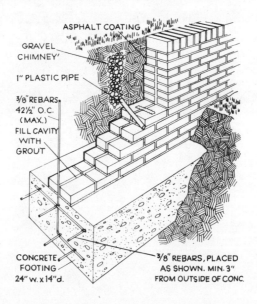

ASPHALT COATING

GRAVEL
CHIMNEY'

1″ PLASTIC PIPE

3/8″ REBARS
42½″ O.C.
(MAX.)
FILL CAVITY
WITH
GROUT

CONCRETE
FOOTING
24″ w. x 14″d.

3/8″ REBARS, PLACED
AS SHOWN. MIN. 3″
FROM OUTSIDE OF CONC.

ing bars in the top of the footing as the concrete is poured.

The concrete footing should be allowed to season for at least a week. Lay up the brick, using your best workmanship and shoved joints, inserting prefabricated steel joint reinforcement where indicated. Some brick must be cut for the insertion of "weep holes" of plastic tubing 1″ in diameter every 4″ along the wall as shown.

Before capping the wall with a solid row of brick laid on edge, pour grout in the gap between the brick to bond the reinforcing bars. Grout is mortar to which water has been added until it is thin enough to pour.

When the wall is completed, brush asphalt, coating on the earth side to make it watertight. A "French drain" of gravel should be placed behind the wall down to the weep hole.

Sandbox

Tools:
> mason's string
> 2″ or 3″ hand level
> brick chisel
> wooden tamper
> wooden screed board

Materials:
> 240 solid brick units 3¾″ × 2¼″ × 8″
>   or 4″ × 8″ × 1⅝″
> about 5 cubic feet of damp, loose
>   sand (¼ ton) (does not include
>   sand for sandbox)
> 1¼ cubic feet of cement or 1¼ bags
>   of Portland cement
> galvanized nails
> ⅝″ exterior grade, rough sawn plywood siding,
>   coated with preservative, cut as follows:
> 4 lengths of 20″ × 55⅜″
> 4 lengths of 2″ × 2″ × 7′
> 4 lengths of 1″ × 4″ × 9′
> 2 lengths of 1″ × 3″ × 10′

Have handy:
> shovel
> wheelbarrow
> garden hose
> garden rake
> broom

A brick sandbox in your back yard will give your children a clean place to have fun, and is not particularly difficult to construct.

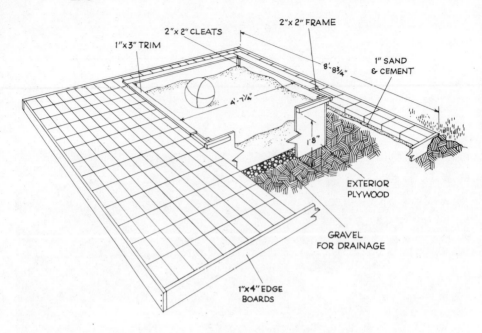

Dig an excavation for the sandbox as indicated in the sketch and install the wooden frame. Fill the sandbox with sand and surround with a 1 × 4 edging as indicated. Spread a dry mixture of 3 parts sand to 1 part cement over the ground area around the sand box, and tamp and grade as necessary to achieve a smooth, even surface. Place solid brick units directly upon this cushion base.

Upon completion of the sandbox, sweep clean sand into cracks between the brick units. Clean with a gentle spray from the garden hose.

Screen

Tools:
> bricklayer's trowel
> mason's string
> mason's hand level
> 2″ and 4″ hand levels
> framing square
> mason's pointing tool
> broad-bladed brick chisel
> wooden float

Materials:
> solid brick units 3¾″ × 2¼″ × 8″
>   4.4 units per square foot of
>   screen; 6.55 units per square foot
>   of solid wall (allow 5% to 25% for
>   waste)
> mortar (consult estimating table)
> .90 cubic feet of concrete per lineal
>   foot for 8″ × 16″ footing
> .66 cubic feet of concrete per lineal
>   foot for 8″ × 12″ footing

Have handy:
> shovel
> wheelbarrow
> garden hose
> garden rake
> hammer
> old broom (short, stiff bristles)
> garden hoe
>   (optional)
> brick cutting equipment

This attractive brick screen will dress up your yard and keep trash cans and installations out of sight.

Some local building regulations do not allow this kind of brick screen; check this when you ask how deep the concrete footing must be.

Study the diagram carefully; this is not a project to rush into. Have some experience behind you first on a less complicated project.

Excavate the footing, making sure it goes below the frost line and that the bottom of the trench is as level as possible. Check it with a straight 2 × 4, 8' long and with a 2' or 4' hand level. Dig out no more than the width of footing wanted. Use the sides of the trench for forming to avoid using extra materials.

CHECK LOCAL
BUILDING CODE
FOR ALLOWABLE
HEIGHT OF SCREEN

CONSTRUCT
FOOTING TO SUIT
LOCAL BUILDING
CODE.

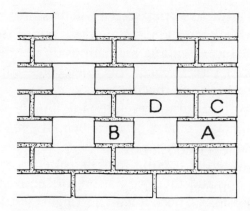

Solid and cut units form a screen pattern

Because the screen's corners must be built as plumb as possible, it's a good idea to begin by laying out the first three courses dry. This will give you a chance to insure a positive layout.

After establishing the solid wall portion, start the pierced-pattern portion at the corner by cutting a crick to a 6″ length (A). Then cut a brick in half and lay in place, centered on the joint where two bricks come together, as shown (B). The cut portion will be visible only from the back side of the wall. Start the next course with a half unit (C), followed by a whole brick (D) spanning over to the middle of the cut brick on the course below. Continue these "stretcher" units for the rest of the course. Repeat the first pattern described after the stretcher course is in place.

Care should be taken during the construction process to avoid putting pressure on the screen — remember that it's only a little over half as heavy as a solid wall.

Steps

Tools:
    trowel
    2′ hand level
    bottomless wooden box
    pointing tool
    brick hammer

Materials:
    For brick 4″ × 8″ × 1⅝″, allow 4.1
        units per square foot of tread
        area and 2.75 units per foot of
        length of the risers
    mortar (see estimating table)

Have handy:
    shovel
    wheelbarrow
    garden hose
    garden hoe
    hand brush
    rent (optional): brick cutter

The importance of an attractive entrance to a house cannot be overemphasized. It provides that first impression and sets the mood for the entire home. An entryway of brick steps adds warmth and character and helps to project a sense of quality and permanence.

Careful planning and execution can provide just the touch you're looking for, at little expense. But good workmanship, patience and some degree of experience are essentials for success with this project.

Lay out the brick in position to see how they will

fit, remembering to allow ⅜" between units to allow for mortar. You may want to rent a brick cutting machine if a great many brick must be cut.

Unless your concrete steps already have an adequate slope, lay the brick units so that they slope forward a little to allow for good drainage. Take particular care with workmanship and tool all mortar joints inward to protect against water penetration.

Mortarless barbecue

Tools:
2′ hand level

Materials:
236 solid brick units 3¾″ × 2¼″ × 8″
2 grill racks

You should be able to build this barbecue in a couple of hours. Bear in mind one important feature of mortarless brick work: *the site you select must be absolutely level and stable.* A concrete slab is best.

Buy your grill racks first; sometimes availability of certain sizes is limited. You can adjust the construction of the barbecue to fit the grill racks you buy.

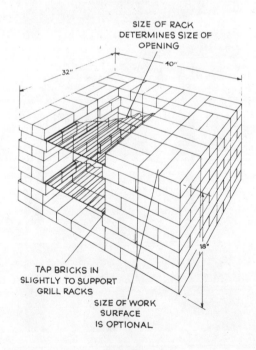

SIZE OF RACK
DETERMINES SIZE OF
OPENING

32″

40″

18″

TAP BRICKS IN
SLIGHTLY TO SUPPORT
GRILL RACKS

SIZE OF WORK
SURFACE
IS OPTIONAL

As you follow the pattern shown, be careful to tap in the brick units that support the grill racks before proceeding to the adjacent optional work surface. The brick units supporting the grill racks should be tapped in with a 2 × 4 length of wood and a hammer. Lay the 2 × 4 edgewise to the row as you tap them in.

Lawn edging

Tools:
> flat-bladed spade
> broom
> shovel
> rubber mallet

Materials:
> 32 solid brick per 10 feet of edging
> 1 ton sand per 110 feet of edging
>   (allows for waste)

Brick edging around lawn and garden areas is both attractive and functional. An almost endless variety of earthy brick colors will enhance your greenery and simplify mowing and trimming chores. And brick edging is perhaps the easiest of all outdoor brick projects.

With the flat-bladed spade, dig up the sod about 4″ deep where the edging is to be. Make a continuous cut

about 10″ wide. Put down a layer of sand and place the brick units flat upon it. Slight curves may be made in the direction of the brick by fanning the units slightly; sharper curves will call for cutting a wedge-shaped unit. When the job is finished, sweep sand between the units and in the trench between the brick edges and the sod.

Changes in weather may make the brick edging rise and fall. You can cope with this easily by removing affected units and smoothing out the gravel underneath.

Stepping stones

Tools:
    2′ hand level
    wooden tamper
    framing square
Materials:
    for 10 squares 16″ × 16″:
        80 solid brick units 3¾″ × 2¼″ × 8″
        10 lengths redwood plank 1″ × 4″ × 6′
        five penny galvanized box
            nails
        3 cubic feet sand (about 260
            pounds)
        1 bag (94 pounds) Portland
            cement

Have handy:
    shovel
    garden hoe

Here's a brick project you can build in just a few hours that will add beauty and interest to your yard for years to come.

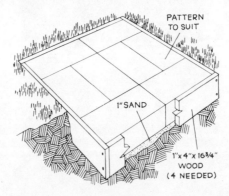

Stepping stones are most conveniently placed about 4″ apart. For each step, excavate a square hole 4″ deep large enough to accommodate a 17½″ frame (outside dimensions) of redwood plank. Position the frame in the excavation so that its top is level with the grass line. Mix 1 part cement to 3 parts sand and spread 1″ to 1½″ of this mixture, dry, in the hole. Tamp it down; add more if needed to bring it near the level of the frame. Lay the brick units on the cushion in the pattern shown; make sure they are flush with the top of the frame.